LOGARI[illegible] EXPONENTIAL FUNCTIONS FOR COMPREHENSIVE STUDY

A STEP-BY-STEP WORKBOOK WITH MULTIPLE QUESTION AND ANSWER FOR PRACTICE.

Adegboye Samuel

For any information, correction or assistance you can send a mail to kunlektrapub@gmail.com

TABLE OF CONTENTS

Unit 1

RULES OF LOGARITHM

A logarithm is a power to which a number must be raised in other to get some other values.

Mathematically to define Logarithm, when you have

$$y = n^x \rightarrow \textit{Exponential form}$$

Where $x \rightarrow$ ***Index***, $n \rightarrow$ ***Base*** *and* $y \rightarrow$ ***Number.***

From the index form above, we can derive the logarithm form, which is;

$$\log_n y = x$$

Summarily,

$$\textit{if } y = n^x; \textit{then } \log_n y = x$$

Let's look into some examples;

$$1000 = 10^3; \textit{then } \log_{10} 1000 = 3$$

$$125 = 5^3; \textit{then } \log_5 125 = 3$$

The examples above show the exponential form and the logarithm form of a function. With this, you can covert from logarithm form to exponential form and vice versa.

The following laws will help your understanding to solve any question on Logarithm.

Law 1: $\log_b P + \log_b Q = \log_b PQ$

How was the law derived?

Let $P = b^X$; *to logarithm form* $\rightarrow \log_b P = X$

$$\boldsymbol{Q = b^Y; to\ logarithm\ form\ \rightarrow\ \log_b Q = Y}$$

Multiply variable P and Q

$$P \times Q = b^X \times b^Y$$

$$PQ = b^{X+Y}$$

Change the exponential equation "$\boldsymbol{PQ = b^{X+Y}}$" to logarithm form;

$$\boldsymbol{\log_b PQ = X + Y}$$

Substitute $\mathbf{X}\ for\ \boldsymbol{\log_b P}\ and\ \boldsymbol{Y}\ for\ \boldsymbol{\log_b Q}$

$$\boldsymbol{\log_b PQ = \log_b P + \log_b Q}$$

Note: This rule is valid when the bases of the logarithm functions are the same. $\boldsymbol{log_a P + log_b Q \neq log_b PQ}$

Law 2: $\boldsymbol{log_b P - log_b Q = log_b \left(\frac{P}{Q}\right)}$

How was the law derived?

Let $\boldsymbol{P = b^X}; to\ logarithm\ form\ \rightarrow\ \boldsymbol{\log_b P = X}$

$$\boldsymbol{Q = b^Y; to\ logarithm\ form\ \rightarrow\ \log_b Q = Y}$$

Multiply variable P and Q

$$P \div Q = b^X \div b^Y$$

$$P \div Q = b^{X-Y}$$

Change the exponential equation "$\boldsymbol{\frac{P}{Q} = b^{X-Y}}$" to logarithm form;

$$\boldsymbol{\log_b \left(\frac{P}{Q}\right) = X - Y}$$

Substitute $\mathbf{X}\ for\ \boldsymbol{\log_b P}\ and\ \boldsymbol{Y}\ for\ \boldsymbol{\log_b Q}$

$$\boldsymbol{\log_b \left(\frac{P}{Q}\right) = \log_b P - \log_b Q}$$

Note: *This rule is valid when the bases of the logarithm functions are the same.* $\boldsymbol{log_a P - log_b Q \neq log_b PQ}$

Law 3: $\log_b P^n = \text{n}\log_b P$

Derivation

Let $\boldsymbol{P = b^X}$; *to logarithm form* $\rightarrow$ $\boldsymbol{\log_b P = X}$

If;

$\boldsymbol{P^n = b^{nX}}$; *to logarithm form* $\boldsymbol{\log_b P^n = nX}$

Substitute;

$$\mathbf{X}\ for\ \boldsymbol{\log_b P}$$

$$\boldsymbol{\log_b P^n = \text{n}\log_b P}$$

Law 4: $\log_P P = 1$

How do I arrive at this?

From the law of indices

$\boldsymbol{P = P^1}$; to logarithm form $\boldsymbol{\log_P P = 1}$

Law 5: $\log_P 1 = 0$

How do I arrive at this?

From the law of indices

$\boldsymbol{1 = P^0}$; to logarithm form $\boldsymbol{\log_P 1 = 0}$

The laws of logarithm given above are the basic rules required to solve any given question on logarithm. This is what we will be using as we resolve miscellaneous questions on logarithm in this workbook.

Question 1: **Convert** $\mathbf{6^3 = 216}$ to logarithm

Solution

$$if\ y = n^x; then\ \log_n y = x$$

$$6^3 = 216$$

Where $x = 3$

$$n = 6$$

$$y = 216$$

Then $6^3 = 216, \log_6 216 = 3$

$$\boldsymbol{log_6\, 216 = 3}$$

Question 2: Convert $\mathbf{0.01^2 = 0.0001}$ to logarithm form.

Solution

$$if\ y = n^x; then\ \log_n y = x$$

$$0.01^2 = 0.0001$$

Where $x = 2$

$$n = 0.01$$

$$y = 0.0001$$

Then $0.01^2 = 0.0001, \log_{0.01} 0.0001 = 2$

$$\mathbf{\log_{0.01} 0.0001 = 2}$$

Question 3: Convert $\mathbf{\log_7 49 = 2}$ to index form.

Solution

$$if \log_n y = x, then\ the\ index\ form\ is\ y = n^x;$$

$$\log_7 49 = 2$$

Where $x = 2$

$$n = 7$$

$$y = 49$$

Then $\log_7 49 = 2,\ y = n^x$

$$\mathbf{49 = 7^2}$$

Question 4: Convert $\mathbf{\log_5 \frac{1}{125} = -3}$ to index form

Solution

$$if \log_n y = x, then\ the\ index\ form\ is\ y = n^x;$$

$$\log_5 \frac{1}{125} = -3$$

Where $x = -3$

$$n = 5$$

$$y = \frac{1}{125}$$

Then$\log_5 \frac{1}{125} = -3,\ \ y = n^x$

$$\frac{1}{125} = \mathbf{5^{-3}}$$

Question 5: Convert $\mathbf{\log_3 27 = x}$ to index form, hence find the value of $\boldsymbol{x}$

Solution

$$if \log_n y = x, then\ the\ index\ form\ is\ y = n^x;$$

$$\mathbf{\log_3 27 = x}$$

Where $x = x$

$$n = 3$$

$$y = 27$$

If $\log_3 27 = x$,

Then, $$y = n^x$$

$$27 = \mathbf{3^x}$$

Solve for the value of x

$$27 = 3^x$$

$$3 \times 3 \times 3 = 3^x$$

$$3^3 = 3^x$$

Since the bases are the same, they will cancel out;

Therefore;

$$\boldsymbol{x = 3}$$

Unit 2

SIMPLIFICATION OF LOGARITHM

Question 1: ***Simplify*** $\log_5 \sqrt{3}$

Solution

From the law of indices

$$\sqrt{3} = 3^{\frac{1}{2}}$$

Therefore;

$$\log_5 \sqrt{3} = \log_5 3^{\frac{1}{2}}$$

From the law of logarithm;

$$\log_b P^n = \mathrm{n}\log_b P$$

Therefore;

$$\log_5 3^{\frac{1}{2}} = \frac{1}{2}\log_5 3$$

$$\log_5 \sqrt{3} = \frac{1}{2}\log_5 3$$

Question 2: ***Simplify*** $\log_7 \sqrt[3]{5} = 5^{\frac{1}{3}}$

Solution

From the law of indices

$$\sqrt[3]{5} = 5^{\frac{1}{3}}$$

Therefore;

$$\log_7 \sqrt[3]{5} = \log_7 5^{\frac{1}{3}}$$

From the law of logarithm;

$$\log_b P^n = \mathrm{n}\log_b P$$

Therefore;

$$\log_7 5^{\frac{1}{3}} = \frac{1}{3}\log_7 5$$

$$\log_7 \sqrt[3]{5} = \frac{1}{3}\log_7 5$$

Question 3: ***Simplify*** $\mathbf{\log_{10} 1000}$

Solution

From the law of indices

$$1000 = 10^3$$

Therefore;

$$\log_{10} 1000 = \log_{10} 10^3$$

From the law of logarithm;

$$\log_b P^n = \text{n}\log_b P$$

Therefore;

$$\log_{10} 10^3 = 3\log_{10} 10$$

Recall;

$$\text{Log}_P P = 1$$

$$3\log_{10} 10 = 3 \times 1 = 3$$

$$\log_{10} 1000 = 3$$

Question 4: ***Simplify*** $\mathbf{\log_{10} 100}$

Solution

From the law of indices

$$100 = 10^2$$

Therefore;

$$\log_{10} 100 = \log_{10} 10^2$$

From the law of logarithm;

$$\log_b P^n = \text{n}\log_b P$$

Therefore;

$$\log_{10} 10^2 = 2\log_{10} 10$$

Recall;

$$\text{Log}_P\, P = 1$$

$$2\log_{10} 10 = 2 \times 1 = 2$$

$$\log_{10} 100 = 2$$

Question 5: ***Simplify*** $\mathbf{\log_5 \sqrt{5}}$

Solution

From the law of indices

$$\sqrt{5} = 5^{\frac{1}{2}}$$

Therefore;

$$\mathbf{\log_5 \sqrt{5}} = \log_5 5^{\frac{1}{2}}$$

From the law of logarithm;

$$\log_b P^n = \text{n}\log_b P$$

Therefore;

$$\log_5 5^{\frac{1}{2}} = \frac{1}{2}\log_5 5$$

Recall;

$$\text{Log}_P\, P = 1$$

$$\frac{1}{2}\log_5 5 = \frac{1}{2} \times 1 = \frac{1}{2}$$

$$\log_5 \sqrt{5} = \frac{1}{2}$$

Question 6: ***Simplify*** $\mathbf{\log_5 0.1}$

Solution

From the law of indices

$$0.1 = \frac{1}{10}$$

Therefore;

$$log_5 \frac{1}{10}$$

From the law of logarithm;

$$log_b P - log_b Q = log_b \left(\frac{P}{Q}\right)$$

Therefore;

$$log_5 \left(\frac{1}{10}\right) = log_5 1 - log_5 10$$

$$= log_5 1 - log_5(2 \times 5)$$

$log_5(2 \times 5) = log_5 2 + log_5 5$

$$= log_5 1 - log_5 2 + log_5 5$$

If $log_p p = 1,\ log_p 1 = 0$

$log_5 5 = 1,\ log_5 1 = 0$

$$= 0 - log_5 2 + 1 = -log_5 2 + 1$$

$$\boldsymbol{log_5 0.1 = 1 - log_5 2}$$

Question 7: ***Simplify*** $\mathbf{\log_5 12 + \log_5 10}$

Solution

From the law of logarithm;

$$log_b P + log_b Q = log_b PQ$$

Therefore;

$$\log_5 12 + \log_5 10 = \log_5 12 + \log_5(2 \times 5)$$

$$= \log_5 12 + \log_5(2 \times 5)$$

$$= \log_5 12 + \log_5 2 + \log_5 5$$

Recall;

$$\text{Log}_P P = 1$$

$$= \log_5 12 + \log_5 2 + 1$$

$$= \log_5(12 \times 2) + 1$$

$$\log_5 12 + \log_5 10 = 1 + \log_5 24$$

Question 8: ***Simplify*** $\mathbf{\log_2 12 + \log_2 5}$

Solution

From the law of logarithm;

$$log_b P + log_b Q = log_b PQ$$

Therefore;

$$\log_2 12 + \log_2 5 = \log_2(12 \times 5)$$

$$= \log_2(12 \times 5)$$

$$= \log_2 60$$

Question 9: ***Simplify*** $\mathbf{\log_7 49 - \log_7 14}$

Solution

From the law of logarithm;

$$log_b P - log_b Q = log_b \left(\frac{P}{Q}\right)$$

Therefore;

$$\mathbf{log_7 49 - log_7 14} = log_7\left(\frac{49}{14}\right)$$

$$= log_7\left(\frac{7}{2}\right)$$

$$= \log_7 7 - \log_7 2$$

$$= 1 - \log_7 2$$

$$\mathbf{log_7 49 - log_7 14 = 1 - log_7 2}$$

Question 10: ***Simplify*** $\mathbf{2log_7 9 - log_7 81}$

Solution

From the law of logarithm;

$$log_b P - log_b Q = log_b\left(\frac{P}{Q}\right)$$

$$\text{nlog}_b P = \log_b P^n$$

Therefore;

$$2\log_7 9 - \log_7 81 = \log_7 9^2 - \log_7 81$$

$$= \log_7 81 - \log_7 81$$

$$= log_7 81 - log_7 81$$

$$= log_7\left(\frac{81}{81}\right)$$

$$= log_7 1$$

Recall;

$$\log_P 1 = 0$$

$$log_7 1 = 0$$

$$2\log_7 9 - \log_7 81 = log_7 1 = 0$$

Question 11: ***Simplify*** $\mathbf{log_3 24 + log_3 15 - log_3 10}$

Solution

From the law of logarithm;

$$log_b P + log_b Q = log_b PQ$$

$$log_b P - log_b Q = log_b \left(\frac{P}{Q}\right)$$

$$\text{n}\log_b P = \log_b P^n$$

Therefore;

$$log_3 24 + log_3 15 - log_3 10$$

$$= log_3 \left(\frac{24 \times 15}{10}\right) = log_3 \left(\frac{360}{10}\right)$$

$$= log_3 36$$

$$= log_3 6^2 = 2\log_3 6$$

$$= 2\log_3(2 \times 3)$$

$$= 2(\log_3 2 + \log_3 3)$$

$$= 2(\log_3 2 + 1)$$

$$log_3 24 + log_3 15 - log_3 10 = 2(\log_3 2 + 1)$$

Question 12: ***Simplify*** $\mathbf{\log_a \frac{5}{7} + \log_a \frac{7}{6} - \log_a \frac{5}{6}}$

Solution

From the law of logarithm;

$$log_b P + log_b Q = log_b PQ$$

$$log_b P - log_b Q = log_b \left(\frac{P}{Q}\right)$$

$$\text{n}\log_b P = \log_b P^n$$

Therefore;

$$\log_a \frac{5}{7} + \log_a \frac{7}{6} - \log_a \frac{5}{6}$$

$$= log_a \left(\frac{5}{7} \times \frac{7}{6} \div \frac{5}{6}\right) = log_a \left(\frac{5}{6} \div \frac{5}{6}\right)$$

$$= log_a\left(\frac{5}{6}\times\frac{6}{5}\right)$$

$$= log_a 1 = 0$$

$$\log_a\frac{5}{7} + \log_a\frac{7}{6} - \log_a\frac{5}{6} = log_a 1 = 0$$

Question 13: ***Simplify*** $\boldsymbol{log_5\frac{4}{5} + log_5\frac{3}{8} - log_5\frac{3}{2}}$

Solution

From the law of logarithm;

$$log_b P + log_b Q = log_b PQ$$

$$log_b P - log_b Q = log_b\left(\frac{P}{Q}\right)$$

$$\text{n}\log_b P = \log_b P^n$$

Therefore;

$$log_5\frac{4}{5} + log_5\frac{3}{8} - log_5\frac{3}{2}$$

$$= log_5\left(\frac{4}{5}\times\frac{3}{8}\div\frac{3}{2}\right) = log_5\left(\frac{12}{40}\div\frac{3}{2}\right)$$

$$= log_5\left(\frac{3}{10}\div\frac{3}{2}\right)$$

$$= log_5\left(\frac{3}{10}\times\frac{2}{3}\right) = log_5\left(\frac{1}{5}\right)$$

$$= log_5\left(\frac{1}{5}\right) = log_5 1 - log_5 5$$

If $\log_p p = 1, \log_p 1 = 0$, then $\log_5 5 = 1, \log_5 1 = 0$

$$= log_5 1 - log_5 5 = 0 - 1 = -1$$

$$log_5\frac{4}{5} + log_5\frac{3}{8} - log_5\frac{3}{2} = -1$$

Question 14: : *if* $\boldsymbol{log_5 2 = 0.431}$ $\boldsymbol{log_5 3 = 0.682}$ ***Find the value*** $\boldsymbol{log_5 0.6 - log_5 1.2 + log_5 1.8}$

Solution

From the law of logarithm;

$$log_b P + log_b Q = log_b PQ$$

$$log_b P - log_b Q = log_b \left(\frac{P}{Q}\right)$$

$$\text{n}\log_b P = \log_b P^n$$

Therefore;

$$\boldsymbol{log_5 0.6 - log_5 1.2 + log_5 1.8}$$

$$log_5 0.6 = log_5 \frac{6}{10}$$

$$log_5 1.2 = log_5 \frac{12}{10}$$

$$log_5 1.8 = log_5 \frac{18}{10}$$

$$= log_5 \frac{6}{10} - log_5 \frac{12}{10} + log_5 \frac{18}{10}$$

$$= log_5 \left(\frac{6}{10} \div \frac{12}{10} \times \frac{18}{10}\right) = log_5 \left(\frac{6}{10} \times \frac{10}{12} \times \frac{18}{10}\right)$$

$$= log_5 \left(\frac{9}{10}\right)$$

$$= log_5 \left(\frac{9}{10}\right) = log_5 3^2 - log_5 10$$

$$= log_5 9 - log_5(2 \times 5) = 2log_5 3 - log_5 2 - log_5 5$$

$$= 2log_5 3 - log_5 2 - log_5 5$$

If $\log_p p = 1$, then $\log_5 5 = 1$

$$= 2log_5 3 - log_5 2 - 1$$

Recall;

$$log_5 2 = 0.431$$

$$log_5 3 = 0.682$$

$$= 2log_5 3 - log_5 2 - 1 = (2 \times 0.682) - 0.431 - 1 = -0.0067$$

$$= log_5 1 - log_5 5 = 0 - 1 = -1$$

$$log_5 \frac{4}{5} + log_5 \frac{3}{8} - log_5 \frac{3}{2} = -1$$

Question 15: *if* $\boldsymbol{log_5 2 = 0.431}$ *and* $\boldsymbol{log_5 3 = 0.682}$ *find the value of* $\boldsymbol{log_5 6}$

Solution

$$\log_5 6 = \log_5(2 \times 3)$$

From the law of logarithm;

$$\log_b P + \log_b Q = \log_b PQ$$

Therefore;

$$\log_5(2 \times 3) = \log_5 2 + \log_5 3$$

If,

$$\log_5 2 = 0.431$$

$$\log_5 3 = 0.682$$

Then;

$$\log_5 2 + \log_5 3 = 0.431 + 0.682$$

$$= 0.431 + 0.682 = 1.113$$

$$\log_5 6 = 1.113$$

Question 16: *if* $\boldsymbol{log_5 2 = 0.431}$ *and* $\boldsymbol{log_5 3 = 0.682}$ *find the value of* $\boldsymbol{log_5 75}$

Solution

$$\log_5 75 = \log_5(25 \times 3)$$

From the law of logarithm;

$$\log_b P + \log_b Q = \log_b PQ$$

Therefore;

$$\log_5(25 \times 3) = \log_5 25 + \log_5 3$$

$$= \log_5 5^2 + \log_5 3$$

$$= 2\log_5 5 + \log_5 3$$

If $\log_p p = 1$

$$\log_5 5 = 1$$

Therefore;

$$2(1) + \log_5 3 = 2 + 0.682 = 2.682$$

$$\log_5 75 = 2.682$$

Question 17: *if* $\boldsymbol{log_5 2 = 0.431}$ *and* $\boldsymbol{log_5 3 = 0.682}$ *find the value of* $\boldsymbol{log_5 1.5}$

Solution

$$log_5 1.5 = log_5\left(\frac{15}{10}\right)$$

Reduce $\frac{15}{10}$ *to the lowest term by dividing the numerator and the denominator by 5.*

$$\frac{15}{10} = \frac{3}{2}$$

Therefore;

$$log_5 1.5 = log_5\left(\frac{3}{2}\right)$$

From the law of logarithm;

$$log_b P - log_b Q = log_b \left(\frac{P}{Q}\right)$$

Therefore;

$$log_5 \left(\frac{3}{2}\right) = log_5 3 - log_5 2$$

If,

$$log_5 2 = 0.431$$

$$log_5 3 = 0.682$$

Then;

$$log_5 3 - log_5 2 = 0.682 - 0.431 = 0.251$$

$$log_5 1.5 = 0.251$$

Question 18: *if* $\boldsymbol{log_5 2 = 0.431}$ *and* $\boldsymbol{log_5 3 = 0.682}$ *find the value of* $\boldsymbol{log_5 \frac{12}{5}}$

Solution

$$log_5 \frac{12}{5}$$

From the law of logarithm;

$$log_b P - log_b Q = log_b \left(\frac{P}{Q}\right)$$

Therefore;

$$log_5 \left(\frac{12}{5}\right) = log_5 12 - log_5 5$$

If $\log_p p = 1$

$$\log_5 5 = 1$$

Recall;

$$\log_5 2 = 0.431$$

$$\log_5 3 = 0.682$$

Then;

$$\log_5 12 - \log_5 5 = \log_5 12 - 1$$

Where $\log_5 12 = \log_5(2 \times 2 \times 3) = \log_5 2 + \log_5 2 + \log_5 3$

Therefore;

$$\log_5 12 - 1 = \log_5 2 + \log_5 2 + \log_5 3 - 1$$

$$= 0.431 + 0.431 + 0.682 - 1 = 1.544 - 1 = 0.544$$

Question 19: *if* $\mathbf{\log_5 2 = 0.431}$ *and* $\mathbf{\log_5 3 = 0.682}$ *find the value of* $\mathbf{\log_5 15}$

Solution

$$\log_5 15 = \log_5(3 \times 5)$$

From the law of logarithm;

$$\log_b P + \log_b Q = \log_b PQ$$

Therefore;

$$\log_5(3 \times 5) = \log_5 3 + \log_5 5$$

If,

$$\log_5 3 = 0.682$$

$$\log_5 5 = 1$$

Then;

$$\log_5 3 + \log_5 5 = 0.682 + 1 = 1.682$$

$$\log_5 6 = 1.682$$

Question 20: *if* $\mathbf{\log_5 2 = 0.431}$ *and* $\mathbf{\log_5 3 = 0.682}$ *find the value of* $\mathbf{\log_5 \frac{1}{2}}$

Solution

From the law of logarithm;

$$log_b P - log_b Q = log_b \left(\frac{P}{Q}\right)$$

Therefore;

$$log_5 \left(\frac{1}{2}\right) = log_5 1 - log_5 2$$

If,

$$log_5 2 = 0.431$$
$$log_5 1 = 0$$

Then;

$$log_5 1 - log_5 2 = 0 - 0.431 = -0.431$$

$$log_5 \left(\frac{1}{2}\right) = -0.431$$

Question 21: *if* $\boldsymbol{log_5 2 = 0.431}$ *and* $\boldsymbol{log_5 3 = 0.682}$ *find the value of* $\boldsymbol{log_5 \sqrt{2}}$

Solution

$$log_5 \sqrt{2} = log_5 2^{\frac{1}{2}}$$

Recall; $\log_b P^n = \mathrm{n}\log_b P$

$$log_5 2^{\frac{1}{2}} = \frac{1}{2}\log_5 2$$

if;

$$log_5 2 = 0.431$$
$$\frac{1}{2}\log_5 2 = \frac{1}{2} \times 0.431 = 0.2155$$

$$log_5 \sqrt{2} = 0.2155$$

Question 22: *If* $\boldsymbol{log_5 2 = 0.431}$ *and* $\boldsymbol{log_5 3 = 0.682}$

find the value of $\boldsymbol{log_5 \frac{3}{4} + log_5 \frac{2}{5} - log_5 \frac{3}{5}}$

Solution

$$log_5 \frac{3}{4} + log_5 \frac{2}{5} - log_5 \frac{3}{5}$$

Let represent each value with a variable such that;

$$A = log_5 \frac{3}{4}$$

$$B = log_5 \frac{2}{5}$$

$$C = log_5 \frac{3}{5}$$

Therefore;

$$log_5 \frac{3}{4} + log_5 \frac{2}{5} - log_5 \frac{3}{5} = A + B - C$$

From the law of logarithm;

$$log_b P + log_b Q = log_b PQ$$

$$log_b P - log_b Q = log_b \frac{P}{Q}$$

Then let's simplify each value

Simplify variable A

$$A = log_5 \frac{3}{4} = log_5 3 - log_5 4$$

$$= log_5 3 - (log_5(2 \times 2))$$

$$= log_5 3 - log_5 2 - log_5 2$$

Recall;

$$log_5 2 = 0.431$$

$$log_5 3 = 0.682$$

Then;

$$= log_5 3 - log_5 2 + log_5 2$$

$$= 0.682 - 0.431 - 0.431 = -0.18$$

$$A = log_5 \frac{3}{4} = -0.18$$

Simplify variable B

$$B = log_5 \frac{2}{5} = log_5 2 - log_5 5$$

$$= log_5 2 - log_5 5$$

$$= log_5 2 - 1$$

$$= 0.431 - 1 = -0.569$$

$$B = log_5 \frac{2}{5} = -0.569$$

Simplify variable C

$$C = log_5 \frac{3}{5} = log_5 3 - log_5 5$$

$$= log_5 3 - log_5 5$$

$$= log_5 3 - 1$$

$$= 0.682 - 1 = -0.318$$

$$C = log_5 \frac{3}{5} = -0.318$$

Substitute the variables with their values;

$$log_5 \frac{3}{4} + log_5 \frac{2}{5} - log_5 \frac{3}{5} = A + B - C$$

$$= -0.18 + (-0.569) - (-0.318)$$

$$= -0.18 - 0.569 + 0.318 = -0.431$$

$$log_5 \frac{3}{4} + log_5 \frac{2}{5} - log_5 \frac{3}{5} = -0.431$$

Unit 3

LOGARITHMIC EQUATIONS

Question 1: ***Solve*** $\boldsymbol{log_2(x^2 - 2x + 5) = 2}$

Solution

$$log_2(x^2 - 2x + 5) = 2$$

To solve the logarithmic equation, convert the logarithm form to index form.

$$log_2(x^2 - 2x + 5) = 2$$

$$(x^2 - 2x + 5) = 2^2$$

$$x^2 - 2x + 5 = 4$$

$$x^2 - 2x + 5 - 4 = 0$$

$$x^2 - 2x + 1 = 0$$

Hence, we have a ***quadratic equation****.*

Therefore, solve the quadratic equation by factorizing.

$$\boldsymbol{x^2 - 2x + 1 = 0}$$

Find two factors that, when ***summed****, gives* $\boldsymbol{-2}$ *(the coefficient of* $\boldsymbol{x}$*), and when* ***multiplied****, it gives the product of the coefficient of* $\boldsymbol{x^2}$ $(\boldsymbol{+1})$ *and the constant* "$\boldsymbol{+1}$"*, which equals* $\boldsymbol{+1}$.

$\boldsymbol{Sum = -2}$ $\quad\quad$ $\boldsymbol{product = +1}$

$-1 - 1 = -2$ $\quad\quad$ $-1 \times (-1) = +1$

The two factors are $\boldsymbol{-1 \ and \ -1}$*, replace* $\boldsymbol{-2x}$ *with* $\boldsymbol{-1x - 1x}$ *in the equation.*

$$x^2 - 2x + 1 = 0$$

$$x^2 - x - x + 1 = 0$$

Factorize the **first two terms** and the **last two terms** *separately using a common factor*

$$x(x-1) - 1(x-1) = 0$$

$$(x-1)(x-1) = 0$$

$$x - 1 = 0 \ or \ x - 1 = 0$$

$$x = 0 + 1 \quad or \quad x = 0 + 1$$

$$x = 1 \ or \ 1$$

$$\boldsymbol{x = 1 \ twice}$$

Question 2: **Solve** $\boldsymbol{log_3(x^2 + 2x + 2) = 0}$

Solution

$$log_3(x^2 + 2x + 2) = 0$$

To solve the logarithmic equation, convert the logarithm form to index form.

$$log_2(x^2 + 2x + 2) = 0$$

$$(x^2 + 2x + 2) = 3^0$$

$$x^2 + 2x + 2 = 1$$

$$x^2 + 2x + 2 - 1 = 0$$

$$x^2 + 2x + 1 = 0$$

hence, we have a ***quadratic equation****.*

Therefore, solve the quadratic equation by factorizing

$$\boldsymbol{x^2 + 2x + 1 = 0}$$

*Find two factors that, when **summed**, gives $\mathbf{+2}$ (the coefficient of $\boldsymbol{x}$), and when **multiplied**, it gives the product of the coefficient of $\boldsymbol{x^2}$ $(\mathbf{+1})$ and the constant "$\mathbf{+1}$", which equals $\mathbf{+1}$.*

$$Sum = +2 \qquad\qquad product = +1$$

$$+1 + 1 = +2 \qquad\qquad +1 \times (+1) = +1$$

The two factors are $\mathbf{+1}$ and $\mathbf{+1}$, replace $\mathbf{+2x}$ with $\mathbf{+1x + 1x}$ in the equation.

$$x^2 + 2x + 1 = 0$$

$$x^2 + x + x + 1 = 0$$

***Factorize** the **first two terms** and the **last two terms** separately using a common factor*

$$x(x + 1) + 1(x + 1) = 0$$

$$(x + 1)(x + 1) = 0$$

$$x + 1 = 0 \; or \; x + 1 = 0$$

$$x = 0 - 1 \quad or \quad x = 0 - 1$$

$$x = -1 \; or - 1$$

$$\boldsymbol{x = -1 \; twice}$$

Question 3: ***Solve*** $\boldsymbol{log_4(x^2 + 15) = 3}$

Solution

$$log_4(x^2 + 15) = 3$$

To solve the logarithmic equation, convert the logarithm form to index form.

$$log_4(x^2 + 15) = 3$$

$$(x^2 + 15) = 4^3$$

$$x^2 + 15 = 4 \times 4 \times 4$$

$$x^2 + 15 = 64$$

$$x^2 + 15 - 64 = 0$$

$$x^2 - 49 = 0$$

*hence, we have a **quadratic equation**.*

Therefore, solve the quadratic equation by factorizing.

$$x^2 - 49 = 0$$

The quadratic equation above takes the form of difference of two square;

$$(a^2 - b^2) = (a + b)(a - b)$$

Therefore;

$$x^2 - 49 = 0$$

$$(x + 7)(x - 7) = 0$$

$$x + 7 = 0 \ \ or \ \ x - 7 = 0$$

$$x = 0 - 7 \ \ or \ \ x = 0 + 7$$

$$\boldsymbol{x = -7 \ or + 7}$$

Question 4: ***Solve*** $\mathbf{log_{10}(2x^2 + 5x - 2) = 1}$

Solution

$$log_{10}(2x^2 + 5x - 2) = 1$$

To solve the logarithmic equation, convert the logarithm form to index form.

$$log_{10}(2x^2 + 5x - 2) = 1$$

$$(2x^2 + 5x - 2) = 10^1$$

$$2x^2 + 5x - 2 = 10$$

$$2x^2 + 5x - 2 - 10 = 0$$

$$2x^2 + 2x - 12 = 0$$

*hence, we have a **quadratic equation**.*

Therefore, solve the quadratic equation by factorizing.

$$\mathbf{2x^2 + 2x - 12 = 0}$$

*Find two factors that, when **summed**, gives* $\mathbf{+2}$ *(the coefficient of* $\mathbf{x}$*), and when **multiplied**, it gives the product of the coefficient of* $\mathbf{x^2}$ $(+\mathbf{2})$ *and the constant* "$\mathbf{-12}$"*, which equals* $\mathbf{-24.}$

$$Sum = +2 \qquad product = -24$$

$$+6 - 4 = +2 \qquad +6 \times (-4) = -24$$

The two factors are $\mathbf{+6\ and - 4}$*, replace* $\mathbf{+2x}$ *with* $\mathbf{+6x - 4x}$ *in the equation.*

$$2x^2 + 2x - 12 = 0$$

$$2x^2 + 6x - 4x - 12 = 0$$

***Factorize** the **first two terms** and the **last two terms** separately using a common factor*

$$2x(x + 3) - 4(x + 3) = 0$$

$$(2x - 4)(x + 3) = 0$$

$$2x - 4 = 0 \ or \ x + 3 = 0$$

$$2x = 0 + 4 \quad or \quad x = 0 - 3$$

$$2x = 4 \quad or \ x = -3$$

$$\frac{2x}{2} = \frac{4}{2} \qquad or \quad x = -3$$

$$x = 2 \qquad or \quad x = -3$$

$$\mathbf{x = 2 \qquad or \quad -3}$$

Question 5: **Solve** $\boldsymbol{log_2(3x^2+8x-1)=1}$

Solution

$$log_2(3x^2+8x-1)=1$$

To solve the logarithmic equation, convert the logarithm form to index form.

$$log_2(3x^2+8x-1)=1$$

$$(3x^2+8x-1)=2^1$$

$$3x^2+8x-1=2$$

$$3x^2+8x-1-2=0$$

$$3x^2+8x-3=0$$

*hence, we have a **quadratic equation**.*

Therefore, solve the quadratic equation by factorizing.

$$3x^2+8x-3=0$$

*Find two factors that, when **summed**, gives* $\mathbf{+8}$ *(the coefficient of* $\boldsymbol{x}$*), and when **multiplied**, it gives the product of the coefficient of* $\boldsymbol{x^2}$ $\mathbf{(+3)}$ *and the constant* **"-3"**, *which equals* $\mathbf{-9}$.

$\boldsymbol{Sum = +8}$ $\boldsymbol{product = -9}$

$+9-1=+8$ $+9\times(-1)=\ -9$

The two factors are $\mathbf{+9}$ $\boldsymbol{and}$ $\mathbf{-1}$, *replace* $\boldsymbol{+8x}$ *with* $\boldsymbol{+9x-x}$ *in the equation.*

$$3x^2+8x-3=0$$

$$3x^2+9x-x-3=0$$

***Factorize** the **first two terms** and the **last two terms** separately using a common factor*

$$3x(x+3)-1(x+3)=0$$

$$(3x - 1)(x + 3) = 0$$

$$3x - 1 = 0 \ \ or \ \ x + 3 = 0$$

$$3x = 0 + 1 \quad or \quad x = 0 - 3$$

$$3x = 1 \quad or \ \ x = -3$$

$$\frac{3x}{3} = \frac{1}{3} \qquad or \qquad x = -3$$

$$x = \frac{1}{3} \qquad or \qquad x = -3$$

$$\boldsymbol{x = \frac{1}{3} \qquad or \qquad -3}$$

Question 6: **Solve** $\boldsymbol{log_{10}(x^2 + 6x + 28) = 2}$

Solution

$$log_{10}(x^2 + 6x + 28) = 2$$

To solve the logarithmic equation, convert the logarithm form to index form.

$$log_{10}(x^2 + 6x + 28) = 2$$

$$(x^2 + 6x + 28) = 10^2$$

$$x^2 + 6x + 28 = 100$$

$$x^2 + 6x + 28 - 100 = 0$$

$$x^2 + 6x - 72 = 0$$

hence, we have a ***quadratic equation****.*

Therefore, solve the quadratic equation by factorizing.

$$x^2 + 6x - 72 = 0$$

Find two factors that, when ***summed****, gives* $\boldsymbol{+6}$ *(the coefficient of* $\boldsymbol{x}$*), and when* ***multiplied****, it gives the product of the* coefficient of $\mathbf{x^2}$ $(\mathbf{+1})$ and the constant "$\mathbf{-72}$", which equals -72.

$$Sum = +6 \qquad product = -72$$

$$+12 - 6 = +6 \qquad +12 \times (-6) = -72$$

The two factors are $\mathbf{+12}$ *and* $\mathbf{-6}$, replace $\mathbf{+6x}$ with $\mathbf{+12x - 6x}$ in the equation.

$$x^2 + 6x - 72 = 0$$

$$x^2 + 12x - 6x - 72 = 0$$

Factorize the **first two terms** and the **last two terms** separately using a common factor

$$x(x + 12) - 6(x + 12) = 0$$

$$(x + 12)(x - 6) = 0$$

$$x + 12 = 0 \ or \ x - 6 = 0$$

$$x = 0 - 12 \quad or \quad x = 0 + 6$$

$$x = -12 \quad or \ x = 6$$

$$\boldsymbol{x = -12 \quad or \ \ 6}$$

Question 7: **Solve** $\boldsymbol{log_3(a^2 + 8a + 21) = 2}$

Solution

$$log_3(a^2 + 8a + 21) = 2$$

To solve the logarithmic equation, convert the logarithm form to index.

$$log_3(a^2 + 8a + 21) = 2$$

$$(a^2 + 8a + 21) = 3^2$$

$$a^2 + 8a + 21 = 9$$

$$a^2 + 8a + 21 - 9 = 0$$

$$a^2 + 8a + 12 = 0$$

*hence, we have a **quadratic equation**.*

Therefore, solve the quadratic equation by factorizing.

$$a^2 + 8a + 12 = 0$$

*Find two factors that, when **summed**, gives* $+8$ *(the coefficient of* a*), and when **multiplied**, it gives the product of the coefficient of* $\boldsymbol{a^2}$ $(+\mathbf{1})$ *and the constant "*$+\mathbf{12}$*", which equals* $+12$.

$Sum\ = +8$ $\qquad$ $product\ = +12$

$+6 + 2 = +8$ $\qquad$ $+6 \times (+2) = +12$

The two factors are $+\mathbf{6}\ \boldsymbol{and} + \mathbf{2}$*, replace* $+\mathbf{8}\boldsymbol{a}$ *with* $+\mathbf{5}\boldsymbol{a} + \mathbf{3}\boldsymbol{a}$ *in the equation.*

$$a^2 + 8a + 12 = 0$$

$$a^2 + 6a + 2a + 12 = 0$$

***Factorize** the **first two terms** and the **last two terms** separately using a common factor*

$$a(a + 6) + 2(a + 6) = 0$$

$$(a + 6)(a + 2) = 0$$

$$a + 6 = 0 \ or \ a + 2 = 0$$

$$a = 0 - 6 \quad or \quad a = 0 - 2$$

$$a = -6 \quad or \ a = -2$$

$$\boldsymbol{a = -6 \qquad or \quad -2}$$

Question 8: ***Solve*** $\boldsymbol{log_{10}(2e^2 - 5e + 3) = 0}$

Solution

$$log_{10}(2e^2 - 5e + 3) = 0$$

To solve the logarithmic equation, convert the logarithm form to index.

$$log_{10}(2e^2 - 5e + 3) = 0$$

$$(2e^2 - 5e + 3) = 10^0$$

$$2e^2 - 5e + 3 = 1$$

$$2e^2 - 5e + 3 - 1 = 0$$

$$2e^2 - 5e + 2 = 0$$

*hence, we have a **quadratic equation**.*

Therefore, solve the quadratic equation by factorizing.

$$2e^2 - 5e + 2 = 0$$

*Find two factors that, when **summed**, gives $\mathbf{-5}$ (the coefficient of e), and when **multiplied**, it gives the product of the coefficient of $\mathbf{e^2}$ $(+\mathbf{2})$ and the constant "$\mathbf{+2}$", which equals $+4$.*

$Sum = -5$ $\qquad$ $product = +4$

$-4 - 1 = -5$ $\qquad$ $-4 \times (-1) = +4$

The two factors are $\mathbf{-4}$ and $\mathbf{-1}$, replace $\mathbf{-5e}$ with $\mathbf{-4e - e}$ in the equation.

$$2e^2 - 5e + 2 = 0$$

$$2e^2 - 4e - e + 2 = 0$$

***Factorize** the **first two terms** and the **last two terms** separately using a common factor*

$$2e(e - 2) - 1(e - 2) = 0$$

$$(2e - 1)(e - 2) = 0$$

$$2e - 1 = 0 \ or \ e - 2 = 0$$

$$2e = 0 + 1 \quad or \quad e = 0 - 2$$

$$2e = 1 \quad or \ e = -2$$

$$\frac{2e}{2} = \frac{1}{2} \qquad or \quad x = -2$$

$$e = \frac{1}{2} \quad or \quad e = -2$$

$$\boldsymbol{e = \frac{1}{2} \quad or \quad -2}$$

Question 9: ***Solve*** $\boldsymbol{log_3(2x^2 - 5x) = 1}$

Solution

$$log_3(2x^2 - 5x) = 1$$

To solve the logarithmic equation, convert the logarithm form to index form.

$$log_3(2x^2 - 5x) = 1$$

$$(2x^2 + 5x) = 3^1$$

$$2x^2 + 5x = 3$$

$$2x^2 + 5x = 3$$

$$2x^2 + 5x - 3 = 0$$

*hence, we have a **quadratic equation**.*

Therefore, solve the quadratic equation by factorizing.

$$2x^2 + 5x - 3 = 0$$

*Find two factors that, when **summed**, gives* $\boldsymbol{+5}$ *(the coefficient of* $\boldsymbol{x}$*), and when **multiplied**, it gives the product of the coefficient of* $\boldsymbol{x^2}$ $(\boldsymbol{+2})$ *and the constant* "$\boldsymbol{-3}$", *which equals* $\boldsymbol{-6}$.

$$Sum = +5 \qquad product = -6$$

$$+6 - 1 = +5 \qquad +6 \times (-1) = -6$$

The two factors are $+\mathbf{6}$ $\boldsymbol{and}$ $-\mathbf{1}$, *replace* $+\mathbf{5x}$ *with* $+\mathbf{6x} - \boldsymbol{x}$ *in the equation.*

$$2x^2 + 5x - 3 = 0$$

$$2x^2 + 6x - x - 3 = 0$$

Factorize *the* ***first two terms*** *and the* ***last two terms*** *separately using a common factor*

$$2x(x + 3) - 1(x + 3) = 0$$

$$(2x - 1)(x + 3) = 0$$

$$2x - 1 = 0 \ or \ x + 3 = 0$$

$$2x = 0 + 1 \quad or \quad x = 0 - 3$$

$$2x = 1 \quad or \ x = -3$$

$$\frac{2x}{2} = \frac{1}{2} \qquad or \quad x = -3$$

$$x = \frac{1}{2} \qquad or \quad x = -3$$

$$\boldsymbol{x = \frac{1}{2} \qquad or \quad -3}$$

Question 10: **Solve** $\boldsymbol{log_2(b^2 - 7b + 14) = 2}$

Solution

$$log_2(b^2 - 7b + 14) = 2$$

To solve the logarithmic equation, convert the logarithm form to index form.

$$log_2(b^2 - 7b + 14) = 2$$

$$(b^2 - 7b + 14) = 2^2$$
$$b^2 - 7b + 14 = 4$$
$$b^2 - 7b + 14 - 4 = 0$$
$$b^2 - 7b + 10 = 0$$

*hence, we have a **quadratic equation**.*

Therefore, solve the quadratic equation by factorizing.

$$b^2 - 7b + 10 = 0$$

*Find two factors that, when **summed**, gives −7 (the coefficient of b), and when **multiplied**, it gives the product of the coefficient of* $\mathbf{b^2}$ $(+\mathbf{1})$ *and the constant* "$\mathbf{+10}$", *which equals* $+10$.

$\mathit{Sum} = -7$ $\qquad$ $\mathit{product} = +10$

$-5 - 2 = -7$ $\qquad$ $-5 \times (-2) = +10$

The two factors are $-\mathbf{5}$ *and* $-\mathbf{2}$, *replace* $-\mathbf{7b}$ *with* $-\mathbf{5b} - \mathbf{2b}$ *in the equation.*

$$b^2 - 7b + 10 = 0$$
$$b^2 - 5b - 2b + 10 = 0$$

***Factorize** the **first two terms** and the **last two terms** separately using a common factor*

$$b(b - 5) - 2(b - 5) = 0$$
$$(b - 2)(b - 5) = 0$$
$$b - 2 = 0 \ \ or \ \ b - 5 = 0$$
$$b = 0 + 2 \quad or \quad b = 0 + 5$$
$$b = 2 \quad or \ \ b = 5$$
$$\boldsymbol{b} = 2 \qquad \boldsymbol{or} \quad \mathbf{5}$$

Question 11: ***Solve*** $\boldsymbol{log_2(x^2 - 5x - 6) = 3}$

Solution

$$log_2(x^2 - 5x - 6) = 3$$

To solve the logarithmic equation, convert the logarithm form to index form.

$$log_2(x^2 - 5x - 6) = 3$$

$$(x^2 - 5x - 6) = 2^3$$

$$x^2 - 5x - 6 = 2 \times 2 \times 2$$

$$x^2 - 5x - 6 = 8$$

$$x^2 - 5x - 6 - 8 = 0$$

$$x^2 - 5x - 14 = 0$$

*hence, we have a **quadratic equation**.*

Therefore, solve the quadratic equation by factorizing.

$$x^2 - 5x - 14 = 0$$

*Find two factors that, when **summed**, gives* -5 *(the coefficient of* $\boldsymbol{x}$*), and when **multiplied**, it gives the product of the coefficient of* $\boldsymbol{x^2}$ $(\boldsymbol{+1})$ *and the constant* **"-14"**, *which equals* $\boldsymbol{-14}$**.**

$\boldsymbol{Sum = -5}$ $\boldsymbol{product = -14}$

$-7 + 2 = -5$ $-7 \times (+2) = -14$

The two factors are $\boldsymbol{-7\ and + 2}$*, replace* $\boldsymbol{-5x}$ *with* $\boldsymbol{-7x + 2x}$ *in the equation.*

$$x^2 - 5x - 14 = 0$$

$$x^2 - 7x + 2x - 14 == 0$$

Factorize the **first two terms** and the **last two terms** separately using a common factor

$$x(x-7)+2(x-7)=0$$

$$(x-7)(x+2)=0$$

$$x-7=0 \ or \ x+2=0$$

$$x=0+7 \quad or \quad x=0-2$$

$$x=7 \quad or \ x=-2$$

$$\boldsymbol{x=7 \quad or \quad -2}$$

Question 12: **Solve** $\boldsymbol{log_{10}(x-8)=1-log_{10}(x+1)}$.

Solution

$$log_{10}(x-8)=1-log_{10}(x+1)$$

$$log_{10}(x-8)+log_{10}(x+1)=1$$

From the law of logarithm;

$$\boldsymbol{log_b P+log_b Q=log_b PQ}$$

Therefore;

$$log_{10}(x-8)(x+1)=1$$

Expand

$$(x-8)(x+1)=x(x+1)-8(x+1)$$

$$=x^2+x-8x-8$$

$$=x^2-7x-8$$

Therefore;

$$log_{10}(x-8)(x+1)=1$$

$$log_{10}x^2-7x-8=1$$

To solve the logarithmic equation, convert the logarithm form to index form.

$$log_{10}x^2 - 7x - 8 = 1$$

$$(x^2 - 7x - 8) = 10^1$$

$$x^2 - 7x - 8 = 10$$

$$x^2 - 7x - 8 - 10 = 0$$

$$x^2 - 7x - 18 = 0$$

*hence, we have a **quadratic equation**.*

Therefore, solve the quadratic equation by factorizing.

$$x^2 - 7x - 18 = 0$$

*Find two factors that, when **summed**, gives −7 (the coefficient of $\boldsymbol{x}$), and when **multiplied**, it gives the product of the coefficient of $\mathbf{x^2}$ $(+\mathbf{1})$ and the constant "$\mathbf{-18}$", which equals* $\mathbf{-18.}$

$Sum = -7$ $\quad$ $product = -18$

$-9 + 2 = -7$ $\quad$ $-9 \times (+2) = -18$

The two factors are $\mathbf{-9}$ $\boldsymbol{and}$ $\mathbf{+\ 2}$, replace $\mathbf{-7}\boldsymbol{x}$ with $\mathbf{-9}\boldsymbol{x} + \mathbf{2}\boldsymbol{x}$ in the equation.

$$x^2 - 7x - 18 = 0$$

$$x^2 - 9x + 2x - 18 = 0$$

***Factorize** the **first two terms** and the **last two terms** separately using a common factor*

$$x(x - 9) + 2(x - 9) = 0$$

$$(x - 9)(x + 2) = 0$$

$$x - 9 = 0 \text{ or } x + 2 = 0$$

$$x = 0 + 9 \quad or \quad x = 0 - 2$$

$$x = 9 \quad or \ x = -2$$

$$\boldsymbol{x = 9 \quad or \quad -2}$$

Question 13: **Express *y* in terms of *x*; $\boldsymbol{\frac{1}{2}log_{10}(y+3) = 2x}$.**

Solution

$$\frac{1}{2}log_2(y+3) = 2x$$

From the laws of logarithm

$$\text{n}\log_b P = \log_b P^n$$

Therefore;

$$\frac{1}{2}log_2(y+3) = 2x$$

$$log_2(y+3)^{\frac{1}{2}} = 2x$$

Change to index form;

$$(y+3)^{\frac{1}{2}} = 2^{2x}$$

Square both sides;

$$\left[(y+3)^{\frac{1}{2}}\right]^2 = (2^{2x})^2$$

$$y + 3 = 2^{2x} \times 2^{2x}$$

$$y + 3 = 2^{4x}$$

$$\boldsymbol{y = 2^{4x} - 3}$$

Question 14: **Express *y* in terms of *x*;**
$\boldsymbol{log_8 2x - log_8 y = 1}$

Solution

$$log_8 2x - log_8 y = 1$$

From the laws of logarithm

$$log_b P - log_b Q = log_b\left(\frac{P}{Q}\right)$$

Therefore;

$$log_8 2x - log_8 y = 1$$

$$log_8\left(\frac{2x}{y}\right) = 1$$

Change to index form;

$$\left(\frac{2x}{y}\right) = 8^1$$

Cross multiply;

$$2x = 8^1 \times y$$

$$2x = 8 \times y$$

$$2x = 8y$$

Divide both sides by 8;

$$\frac{2x}{8} = \frac{8y}{8}$$

$$\boldsymbol{y = \frac{x}{4}}$$

Question 15: ***Solve for x;*** $\mathbf{log}_{\sqrt{2}}\,\mathbf{8} = \boldsymbol{x}$

Solution

$$\log_{\sqrt{2}} 8 = x$$

To solve the logarithmic equation, convert the logarithm form to index form.

$$\log_{\sqrt{2}} 8 = x$$

$$8 = \sqrt{2}^x$$

$$2 \times 2 \times 2 = 2^{\frac{1}{2}x}$$

$$2^3 = 2^{\frac{1}{2}x}$$

Since the equation have the same base, both will be cancelled;

$$3 = \frac{x}{2}$$

Cross multiply;

$$x = 2 \times 3 = 6$$

$$\boldsymbol{x = 6}$$

Question 16: **Solve for x; $\mathbf{\log_2 4^{x+1} = 5}$**

Solution

$$\mathbf{\log_2 4^{x+1} = 5}$$

To solve the logarithmic equation, convert the logarithm form to index form.

$$\mathbf{\log_2 4^{x+1} = 5}$$

$$\mathbf{4^{x+1}} = 2^5$$

$$\mathbf{(2^2)^{x+1}} = 2^5$$

$$2^{\mathbf{2x+2}} = 2^5$$

Since the equation have the same base, both will be cancelled;

$$\mathbf{2x + 2} = 5$$

$$\mathbf{2}x = 5 - 2$$

$$\mathbf{2}x = 3$$

Divide both sides by 2;

$$\frac{\mathbf{2}x}{\mathbf{2}} = \frac{3}{2}$$

$$\boldsymbol{x} = \frac{3}{2}$$

Unit 4

LOGARITHMS OF NUMBERS GREATER THAN 1

The logarithm of a number is in two parts;

1. The integer part (also called characteristics): *The characteristic is known as the power in which 10 is raised, when it is written in standard form.*
2. The decimal fraction (mantissa): *The mantissa is gotten from the logarithm table.*

For example the log of **274.5** is **2.4386,** from the logarithm table.

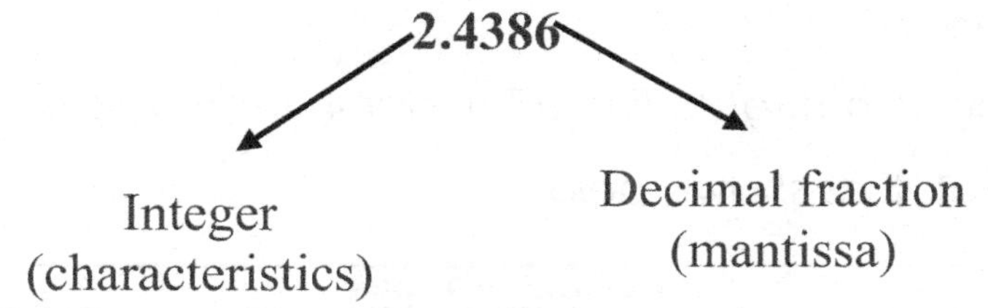

Step required to find the Logarithm of a Number using a Logarithm Table.

a. Write the number in standard form.

b. From the Logarithm table, find the fractional part of the number.

c. Write the logarithm value of the number by combining the integer and the decimal fraction.

(the integer is the value of the power 10 is raised while the decimal fraction is the value you got from the logarithm table).

Question 1: ***Evaluate* $\log 2.745$ *using logarithm table***

Solution

To find $\log 2.745$, *write the number in standard form.*

$$\log 2.745 = \log(2.745 \times 10^0)$$

$$\log 2.745 = \log 2.745 + \log 10^0$$

$$\log 2.745 = \log 2.745 + 0$$

The power of $\mathbf{10}$ *which is* $\mathbf{0}$ *is called* ***the Integer or characteristics.***

The ***decimal fraction*** *or* ***mantissa*** *is determined in the Logarithm table.*

From the logarithm table find 27 under 4, then add mean difference of 5 as shown below.

Logarithm Table

											Mean Differences								
	0	1	2	3	4	5	6	7	8	9	1	2	3	4	5	6	7	8	9
10	0000	0043	0086	0128	0017	0212	0253	0294	0334	0374	4	8	12	17	21	25	29	33	37
11	0414	0453	0492	0531	0569	0607	0645	0682	0719	0755	4	8	11	15	19	23	26	30	34
12	0792	0828	0864	0899	0934	0969	1004	1038	1072	1106	3	7	10	14	17	21	24	28	31
13	1139	1173	1206	1239	1271	1303	1335	1367	1399	1430	3	6	10	13	16	19	23	26	29
14	1461	1492	1523	1553	1584	1614	1644	1673	1703	1732	3	6	9	12	15	18	21	24	27
15	1761	1790	1818	1847	1875	1903	1931	1959	1987	2014	3	6	8	11	14	17	20	22	25
16	2041	2068	2095	2122	2148	2175	2201	2227	2253	2279	3	5	8	11	13	16	18	21	24
17	2304	2330	2355	2380	2405	2430	2455	2480	2504	2529	2	5	7	10	12	15	17	20	22
18	2553	2577	2601	2625	2648	2672	2695	2718	2742	2765	2	5	7	9	12	14	16	19	21
19	2788	2810	2833	2856	2878	2900	2923	2945	2967	2989	2	4	7	9	11	13	16	18	20
20	3010	3032	3054	3075	3096	3118	3139	3160	3181	3201	2	4	6	8	11	13	15	17	19
21	3222	3243	3263	3284	3304	3324	3345	3365	3385	3404	2	4	6	8	10	12	14	16	18
22	3424	3444	3464	3483	3502	3522	3541	2560	3579	3598	2	4	6	8	10	12	14	15	17
23	3617	3636	3655	3674	3692	3711	3729	3747	3766	3784	2	4	6	7	9	11	13	15	17
24	3802	3820	3838	3856	3874	3892	3909	3927	3945	3962	2	4	5	7	9	11	12	14	16
25	3979	3997	4014	4031	4048	4065	4082	4099	4116	4133	2	3	5	7	9	10	12	14	15
26	4150	4166	4183	4200	4216	4232	4249	4265	4281	4298	2	3	5	7	8	10	11	13	15
27	4314	4330	4346	4362	4378	4393	4409	4425	4440	4456	2	3	5	6	8	9	11	13	14
28	4472	4487	4502	451[illegible]	[illegible]	4548	4564	4579	4594	4609	2	3	5	[illegible]	[illegible]	9	11	12	14
29	4624	4639	4654	466[illegible]	[illegible]	4698	4713	4728	4742	4757	1	3	4	6	[illegible]	9	10	12	13
30	4771	4786	4800	4814	4829	4843	4857	4871	4886	4900	1	3	4	6	7	9	10	11	13

4378 + 8 = 438

Therefore;

$$\log 2.745 = \log 2.745 + 0$$

$$\log 2.745 = \mathbf{0.4386 + 0 = 0.4386}$$

$$\log 2.745 = \mathbf{0.4386}$$

Question 2: ***Determine the logarithm of 27.45 using logarithm table.***

Solution

To find $\log 27.45$, *write the number in standard form.*

$$\mathbf{27.45} = 2.745 \times 10^{\mathbf{1}}$$

$$\log 27.45 = \log(2.745 \times 10^{\mathbf{1}})$$

$$\log 27.45 = \log 2.745 + \log 10^{\mathbf{1}}$$

$$\log 27.45 = \log 2.745 + 1$$

The power of **10** *which is* **1** *from standard form is called* ***the Integer or characteristics.***

The ***decimal fraction*** *or* ***mantissa*** *is determined in the Logarithm table.*

From the logarithm table find 27 under 4, then add mean difference of 5 as shown below.

Note: common Logarithm are in base 10

Logarithm Table

											Mean Differences								
	0	1	2	3	4	5	6	7	8	9	1	2	3	4	5	6	7	8	9
10	0000	0043	0086	0128	0017	0212	0253	0294	0334	0374	4	8	12	17	21	25	29	33	37
11	0414	0453	0492	0531	0569	0607	0645	0682	0719	0755	4	8	11	15	19	23	26	30	34
12	0792	0828	0864	0899	0934	0969	1004	1038	1072	1106	3	7	10	14	17	21	24	28	31
13	1139	1173	1206	1239	1271	1303	1335	1367	1399	1430	3	6	10	13	16	19	23	26	29
14	1461	1492	1523	1553	1584	1614	1644	1673	1703	1732	3	6	9	12	15	18	21	24	27
15	1761	1790	1818	1847	1875	1903	1931	1959	1987	2014	3	6	8	11	14	17	20	22	25
16	2041	2068	2095	2122	2148	2175	2201	2227	2253	2279	3	5	8	11	13	16	18	21	24
17	2304	2330	2355	2380	2405	2430	2455	2480	2504	2529	2	5	7	10	12	15	17	20	22
18	2553	2577	2601	2625	2648	2672	2695	2718	2742	2765	2	5	7	9	12	14	16	19	21
19	2788	2810	2833	2856	2878	2900	2923	2945	2967	2989	2	4	7	9	11	13	16	18	20
20	3010	3032	3054	3075	3096	3118	3139	3160	3181	3201	2	4	6	8	11	13	15	17	19
21	3222	3243	3263	3284	3304	3324	3345	3365	3385	3404	2	4	6	8	10	12	14	16	18
22	3424	3444	3464	3483	3502	3522	3541	2560	3579	3598	2	4	6	8	10	12	14	15	17
23	3617	3636	3655	3674	3692	3711	3729	3747	3766	3784	2	4	6	7	9	11	13	15	17
24	3802	3820	3838	3856	3874	3892	3909	3927	3945	3962	2	4	5	7	9	11	12	14	16
25	3979	3997	4014	4031	4048	4065	4082	4099	4116	4133	2	3	5	7	9	10	12	14	15
26	4150	4166	4183	4200	4216	4232	4249	4265	4281	4298	2	3	5	7	[illegible]	10	11	13	15
27	4314	4330	4346	4362	4378	4393	4409	4425	4440	4456	2	3	5	6	8	9	11	13	14
28	4472	4487	4502	451[illegible]	4533	4548	4564	4579	4594	4609	2	3	5	6	8	9	11	12	14
29	4624	4639	4654	466[illegible]	4683	4698	4713	4728	4742	4757	1	3	4	6	7	9	10	12	13
30	4771	4786	4800	4814	4829	4843	4857	4871	4886	4900	1	3	4	6	7	9	10	11	13

4378 + 8 = 4386

Therefore;

$$\log 27.45 = \log 2.745 + 1$$

$$\log 27.45 = \mathbf{0.4386 + 1 = 1.4386}$$

$$\log 27.45 = \mathbf{1.4386}$$

Question 3: ***Determine the logarithm of 274.5 using logarithm table.***

Solution

To find $\log 274.5$, *write the number in standard form.*

$$\mathbf{274.5} = 2.745 \times 10^2$$

$$\log 274.5 = \log(2.745 \times 10^2)$$

$$\log 274.5 = \log 2.745 + \log 10^2$$

$$\log 274.5 = \log 2.745 + 2$$

The power of $\mathbf{10}$ *which is* $\mathbf{2}$ *from standard form is called* ***the Integer or characteristics.***

*The **decimal fraction** or **mantissa** is determined in the Logarithm table.*

From the logarithm table find 27 under 4, then add mean difference of 5 as shown below.

Logarithm Table

											Mean Differences								
	0	1	2	3	4	5	6	7	8	9	1	2	3	4	5	6	7	8	9
10	0000	0043	0086	0128	0017	0212	0253	0294	0334	0374	4	8	12	17	21	25	29	33	37
11	0414	0453	0492	0531	0569	0607	0645	0682	0719	0755	4	8	11	15	19	23	26	30	34
12	0792	0828	0864	0899	0934	0969	1004	1038	1072	1106	3	7	10	14	17	21	24	28	31
13	1139	1173	1206	1239	1271	1303	1335	1367	1399	1430	3	6	10	13	16	19	23	26	29
14	1461	1492	1523	1553	1584	1614	1644	1673	1703	1732	3	6	9	12	15	18	21	24	27
15	1761	1790	1818	1847	1875	1903	1931	1959	1987	2014	3	6	8	11	14	17	20	22	25
16	2041	2068	2095	2122	2148	2175	2201	2227	2253	2279	3	5	8	11	13	16	18	21	24
17	2304	2330	2355	2380	2405	2430	2455	2480	2504	2529	2	5	7	10	12	15	17	20	22
18	2553	2577	2601	2625	2648	2672	2695	2718	2742	2765	2	5	7	9	12	14	16	19	21
19	2788	2810	2833	2856	2878	2900	2923	2945	2967	2989	2	4	7	9	11	13	16	18	20
20	3010	3032	3054	3075	3096	3118	3139	3160	3181	3201	2	4	6	8	11	13	15	17	19
21	3222	3243	3263	3284	3304	3324	3345	3365	3385	3404	2	4	6	8	10	12	14	16	18
22	3424	3444	3464	3483	3502	3522	3541	2560	3579	3598	2	4	6	8	10	12	14	15	17
23	3617	3636	3655	3674	3692	3711	3729	3747	3766	3784	2	4	6	7	9	11	13	15	17
24	3802	3820	3838	3856	3874	3892	3909	3927	3945	3962	2	4	5	7	9	11	12	14	16
25	3979	3997	4014	4031	4048	4065	4082	4099	4116	4133	2	3	5	7	9	10	12	14	15
26	4150	4166	4183	4200	4216	4232	4249	4265	4281	4298	2	3	5	7	[illegible]	10	11	13	15
27	4314	4330	4346	4362	4378	4393	4409	4425	4440	4456	2	3	5	6	8	9	11	13	14
28	4472	4487	4502	4518	[illegible]	4548	4564	4579	4594	4609	2	3	5	6	[illegible]	9	11	12	14
29	4624	4639	4654	4669	[illegible]	4698	4713	4728	4742	4757	1	3	4	6	7	9	10	12	13
30	4771	4786	4800	4814	4829	4843	4857	4871	4886	4900	1	3	4	6	7	9	10	11	13

4378 + 8 = 4386

Therefore;

$$\mathbf{log}\, 274.5 = \log 2.745 + 2$$

$$\mathbf{log}\, 274.5 = \mathbf{0.4386 + 2}$$

$$\mathbf{log}\, 27.45 = \mathbf{2.4386}$$

Question 4: ***Determine the logarithm of 2745 using logarithm table.***

Solution

To find $\mathbf{log}\, 2745$, *write the number in standard form.*

$$\mathbf{2745} = 2.745 \times 10^3$$

$$\mathbf{log}\, 2745 = \log(2.745 \times 10^3)$$

$$\mathbf{log}\, 2745 = \log 2.745 + \log 10^3$$

$$\log 2745 = \log 2.745 + 3$$

The power of **10** *which is* **3** *from standard form is called* ***the Integer or characteristics.***

The ***decimal fraction*** *or* ***mantissa*** *is determined in the Logarithm table.*

From the logarithm table find 27 under 4, then add mean difference of 5 as shown below.

Logarithm Table

	0	1	2	3	4	5	6	7	8	9	Mean Differences 1	2	3	4	5	6	7	8	9
10	0000	0043	0086	0128	0017	0212	0253	0294	0334	0374	4	8	12	17	21	25	29	33	37
11	0414	0453	0492	0531	0569	0607	0645	0682	0719	0755	4	8	11	15	19	23	26	30	34
12	0792	0828	0864	0899	0934	0969	1004	1038	1072	1106	3	7	10	14	17	21	24	28	31
13	1139	1173	1206	1239	1271	1303	1335	1367	1399	1430	3	6	10	13	16	19	23	26	29
14	1461	1492	1523	1553	1584	1614	1644	1673	1703	1732	3	6	9	12	15	18	21	24	27
15	1761	1790	1818	1847	1875	1903	1931	1959	1987	2014	3	6	8	11	14	17	20	22	25
16	2041	2068	2095	2122	2148	2175	2201	2227	2253	2279	3	5	8	11	13	16	18	21	24
17	2304	2330	2355	2380	2405	2430	2455	2480	2504	2529	2	5	7	10	12	15	17	20	22
18	2553	2577	2601	2625	2648	2672	2695	2718	2742	2765	2	5	7	9	12	14	16	19	21
19	2788	2810	2833	2856	2878	2900	2923	2945	2967	2989	2	4	7	9	11	13	16	18	20
20	3010	3032	3054	3075	3096	3118	3139	3160	3181	3201	2	4	6	8	11	13	15	17	19
21	3222	3243	3263	3284	3304	3324	3345	3365	3385	3404	2	4	6	8	10	12	14	16	18
22	3424	3444	3464	3483	3502	3522	3541	2560	3579	3598	2	4	6	8	10	12	14	15	17
23	3617	3636	3655	3674	3692	3711	3729	3747	3766	3784	2	4	6	7	9	11	13	15	17
24	3802	3820	3838	3856	3874	3892	3909	3927	3945	3962	2	4	5	7	9	11	12	14	16
25	3979	3997	4014	4031	4048	4065	4082	4099	4116	4133	2	3	5	7	9	10	12	14	15
26	4150	4166	4183	4200	4216	4232	4249	4265	4281	4298	2	3	5	7	[illegible]	10	11	13	15
27	4314	4330	4346	4362	4378	4393	4409	4425	4440	4456	2	3	5	6	8	9	11	13	14
28	4472	4487	4502	4518	4533	4548	4564	4579	4594	4609	2	3	5	6	8	9	11	12	14
29	4624	4639	4654	4669	4683	4698	4713	4728	4742	4757	1	3	4	6	7	9	10	12	13
30	4771	4786	4800	4814	4829	4843	4857	4871	4886	4900	1	3	4	6	7	9	10	11	13

4378 + 8 = 4386

Therefore;

$$\log 2745 = \log 2.745 + 3$$

$$\log 2745 = \mathbf{0.4386 + 3}$$

$$\log 2745 = \mathbf{3.4386}$$

Summarily, from question 27 to 30

$$\log 2.745 = \mathbf{0.4386}$$

$$\log 27.45 = \mathbf{1.4386}$$

$$\log 274.5 = \mathbf{2.4386}$$

$$\log 2745 = \mathbf{3.4386}$$

all in base 10.

As the decimal point moves forward, the value of **integer or characteristics** increases.

Question 5: ***Determine the logarithm of 24.86 using logarithm table.***

Solution

To find $\mathbf{log}\,24.86$, *write the number in standard form.*

$$\mathbf{24.86} = 2.486 \times 10^{\mathbf{1}}$$

$$\mathbf{log}\,24.86 = \log(2.486 \times 10^{1})$$

$$\mathbf{log}\,2486 = \log 2.486 + \log 10^{1}$$

$$\mathbf{log}\,2486 = \log 2.486 + 1$$

The power of $\mathbf{10}$ *which is* $\mathbf{1}$ *from standard form is called* ***the Integer or characteristics.***

The ***decimal fraction*** *or* ***mantissa*** *is determined in the Logarithm table.*

From the logarithm table find $\mathbf{24}$ *under* $\mathbf{8}$*, then add mean difference of* $\mathbf{6}$ *as shown below.*

Check the logarithm table at the later-end pages of the book

$24\ under\ 8 \rightarrow \mathbf{3945}$

$Mean\ difference\ of\ \mathbf{6} \rightarrow \mathbf{11}$

$$\mathbf{3945} + \mathbf{11} = \mathbf{3956}$$

Therefore;

$$\mathbf{log}\,2486 = \log 2.486 + 1$$

$$\mathbf{log}\,2486 = \mathbf{0.3956} + 1$$

$$\mathbf{log}\,\mathbf{24.86} = \mathbf{1.3956}$$

Question 6: **Determine the logarithm of 361.4 using logarithm table.**

Solution

To find $\log 361.4$, *write the number in standard form.*

$$361.4 = 3.614 \times 10^2$$

$$\log 361.4 = \log(3.614 \times 10^2)$$

$$\log 361.4 = \log 3.614 + \log 10^2$$

$$\log 361.4 = \log 3.614 + 2$$

The power of **10** *which is* **2** *from standard form is called* ***the Integer or characteristics.***

The ***decimal fraction*** *or* ***mantissa*** *is determined in the Logarithm table.*

From the logarithm table find **36** *under* **1**, *then add mean difference of* **4** *as shown below.*

Check the logarithm table at the later-end pages of the book

$\mathbf{36}\ under\ 1 \rightarrow 5575$

$Mean\ difference\ of\ 4 \rightarrow 5$

$$5575 + 5 = 5580$$

Therefore;

$$\log 361.4 = \log 3.614 + 2$$

$$\log 361.4 = 0.5580 + 2$$

$$\log 361.4 = 2.5580$$

Question 7: **Determine the logarithm of 1308 using logarithm table.**

Solution

To find $\log \mathbf{1308}$, *write the number in standard form.*

$$\mathbf{1308} = \mathbf{1.308} \times 10^3$$

$$\log 1308 = \log(1.308 \times 10^3)$$

$$\log 361.4 = \log 1.308 + \log 10^3$$

$$\log 361.4 = \log 1.308 + 3$$

The power of **10** *which is* **3** *from standard form is called* ***the Integer or characteristics.***

The ***decimal fraction*** *or* ***mantissa*** *is determined in the Logarithm table.*

From the logarithm table find **13** *under* **0**, *then add mean difference of* **8** *as shown below.*

Check the logarithm table at the later-end pages of the book

$\mathbf{13}\ under\ 0 \rightarrow 1139$

$Mean\ difference\ of\ 8 \rightarrow \mathbf{26}$

$$1139 + 26 = 1165$$

Therefore;

$$\log 1308 = \log 1.308 + 3$$

$$\log 1308 = 0.1165 + 3$$

$$\log \mathbf{1308} = \mathbf{3.1165}$$

Question 8: ***Determine the logarithm of*** $\mathbf{361.4}$ ***using logarithm table.***

Solution

To find $\log \mathbf{5.858}$, *write the number in standard form.*

$$\mathbf{5.858} = \mathbf{5.858} \times 10^0$$

$$\log 5.858 = \log(5.858 \times 10^0)$$

$$\log 5.858 = \log 5.858 + \log 10^0$$

$$\log 5.858 = \log 5.858 + 0$$

The power of **10** *which is* **0** *from standard form is called* ***the Integer or characteristics.***

The ***decimal fraction*** *or* ***mantissa*** *is determined in the Logarithm table.*

From the logarithm table find **58** *under* **5***, then add mean difference of* **8** *as shown below.*

Check the logarithm table at the later-end pages of the book

$\mathbf{58}\ under\ 5 \rightarrow \mathbf{7672}$

$Mean\ difference\ of\ 8 \rightarrow \mathbf{7}$

$$\mathbf{7672}\ + \quad 7 \quad = \mathbf{7679}$$

Therefore;

$$\log 5.858 = \log 5.858 + \log 10^0$$

$$\log 5.858 = 0.7679 + 0$$

$$\mathbf{\log 5.858 = 0.7679}$$

Question 9: ***Determine the logarithm of*** $\mathbf{173.5}$ ***using logarithm table.***

Solution

To find $\mathbf{\log 173.5}$, *write the number in standard form.*

$$\mathbf{173.5} = \mathbf{173.5} \times 10^2$$

$$\log 173.5 = \log(1.735 \times 10^2)$$

$$\log 173.5 = \log 1.735 + \log 10^2$$

$$\log 173.5 = \log 1.735 + 2$$

The power of **10** *which is* **2** *from standard form is called* ***the Integer or characteristics.***

Check the logarithm table at the later-end pages of the book

The ***decimal fraction*** *or* ***mantissa*** *is determined in the Logarithm table.*

From the logarithm table find **17** *under* **3**, *then add mean difference of* **5** *as shown below.*

$\mathbf{17}\ under\ 3 \rightarrow \mathbf{2380}$

$Mean\ difference\ of\ 5 \rightarrow \mathbf{12}$

$$\mathbf{2380} + \mathbf{12} = \mathbf{2392}$$

Therefore;

$$\mathbf{log}\,173.5 = \log 1.735 + \log 10^{2}$$

$$\mathbf{log}\,173.5 = \log 1.735 + 2$$

$$\mathbf{log\,173.5 = 2.2392}$$

Unit 5

LOGARITHMS OF NUMBERS LESS THAN 1

Step required to find the Logarithm of a Number using a Logarithm Table.

a. Write the number in standard form.
b. From the Logarithm table, find the fractional part of the number.
c. Write the logarithm value of the number by combining the integer and the decimal fraction.
(the integer is the value of the power 10 is raised while the decimal fraction is the value you got from the logarithm table).

Question 1: ***Determine the logarithm of 0.2745 using logarithm table.***

Solution

To find $\mathbf{log}\,0.2745$*, write the number in standard form.*

$$\mathbf{0.2745} = 2.745 \times 10^{-1}$$

$$\mathbf{log}\,0.2745 = \log(2.745 \times 10^{-1})$$

$$\mathbf{log}\,0.2745 = \log 2.745 + \log 10^{-1}$$

$$\mathbf{log}\,0.2745 = \log 2.745 - 1$$

The power of $\mathbf{10}$ *which is* $-\mathbf{1}$ *is called* ***the Integer or characteristics.***

The **decimal fraction** or **mantissa** is determined in the Logarithm table.

From the logarithm table find 27 under 4, then add mean difference of 5 as shown below.

Logarithm Table

	0	1	2	3	4	5	6	7	8	9	Mean Differences 1	2	3	4	5	6	7	8	9
10	0000	0043	0086	0128	0017	0212	0253	0294	0334	0374	4	8	12	17	21	25	29	33	37
11	0414	0453	0492	0531	0569	0607	0645	0682	0719	0755	4	8	11	15	19	23	26	30	34
12	0792	0828	0864	0899	0934	0969	1004	1038	1072	1106	3	7	10	14	17	21	24	28	31
13	1139	1173	1206	1239	1271	1303	1335	1367	1399	1430	3	6	10	13	16	19	23	26	29
14	1461	1492	1523	1553	1584	1614	1644	1673	1703	1732	3	6	9	12	15	18	21	24	27
15	1761	1790	1818	1847	1875	1903	1931	1959	1987	2014	3	6	8	11	14	17	20	22	25
16	2041	2068	2095	2122	2148	2175	2201	2227	2253	2279	3	5	8	11	13	16	18	21	24
17	2304	2330	2355	2380	2405	2430	2455	2480	2504	2529	2	5	7	10	12	15	17	20	22
18	2553	2577	2601	2625	2648	2672	2695	2718	2742	2765	2	5	7	9	12	14	16	19	21
19	2788	2810	2833	2856	2878	2900	2923	2945	2967	2989	2	4	7	9	11	13	16	18	20
20	3010	3032	3054	3075	3096	3118	3139	3160	3181	3201	2	4	6	8	11	13	15	17	19
21	3222	3243	3263	3284	3304	3324	3345	3365	3385	3404	2	4	6	8	10	12	14	16	18
22	3424	3444	3464	3483	3502	3522	3541	2560	3579	3598	2	4	6	8	10	12	14	15	17
23	3617	3636	3655	3674	3692	3711	3729	3747	3766	3784	2	4	6	7	9	11	13	15	17
24	3802	3820	3838	3856	3874	3892	3909	3927	3945	3962	2	4	5	7	9	11	12	14	16
25	3979	3997	4014	4031	4048	4065	4082	4099	4116	4133	2	3	5	7	9	10	12	14	15
26	4150	4166	4183	4200	4216	4232	4249	4265	4281	4298	2	3	5	7	[illegible]	10	11	13	15
27	4314	4330	4346	4362	4378	4393	4409	4425	4440	4456	2	3	5	6	8	9	11	13	14
28	4472	4487	4502	4518	[illegible]	4548	4564	4579	4594	4609	2	3	5	6	[illegible]	9	11	12	14
29	4624	4639	4654	4669	[illegible]	4698	4713	4728	4742	4757	1	3	4	6	7	9	10	12	13
30	4771	4786	4800	4814	4829	4843	4857	4871	4886	4900	1	3	4	6	7	9	10	11	13

4378 + 8 = 4386

Therefore;

The answer to log of numbers less than 1 will be given in two forms for clarification.

- Bar notation form
- Calculator's result.

$$for\ bar\ notation\ \mathbf{log}\,2.745 = \mathbf{\bar{1}.4386}$$

$$Calculator's\ result\ \mathbf{log}\,2.745 = \mathbf{0.4386 - 1 = -0.5614}$$

$$\mathbf{log\,0.}02745 = \mathbf{\bar{1}.4386}\ \boldsymbol{or} - \mathbf{0.5614}$$

Note: ***for consistency, bar notation result will be used***

Question 2: ***Evaluate 0.02745 using logarithm table.***

Solution

***To find* log** 0.02745*, write the number in standard form.*

$$\mathbf{0.02745} = 2.745 \times 10^{-2}$$

$$\mathbf{log}\, 0.02745 = \log(2.745 \times 10^{-2})$$

$$\mathbf{log}\, 0.02745 = \log 2.745 + \log 10^{-2}$$

$$\mathbf{log}\, 0.02745 = \log 2.745 - 2$$

The power of **10** *which is* $-\mathbf{2}$ *is called* ***the Integer or characteristics.***

The ***decimal fraction*** *or* ***mantissa*** *is determined in the Logarithm table.*

From the logarithm table find 27 under 4, then add mean difference of 5 as shown below.

Logarithm Table

											Mean Differences								
	0	1	2	3	4	5	6	7	8	9	1	2	3	4	5	6	7	8	9
10	0000	0043	0086	0128	0017	0212	0253	0294	0334	0374	4	8	12	17	21	25	29	33	37
11	0414	0453	0492	0531	0569	0607	0645	0682	0719	0755	4	8	11	15	19	23	26	30	34
12	0792	0828	0864	0899	0934	0969	1004	1038	1072	1106	3	7	10	14	17	21	24	28	31
13	1139	1173	1206	1239	1271	1303	1335	1367	1399	1430	3	6	10	13	16	19	23	26	29
14	1461	1492	1523	1553	1584	1614	1644	1673	1703	1732	3	6	9	12	15	18	21	24	27
15	1761	1790	1818	1847	1875	1903	1931	1959	1987	2014	3	6	8	11	14	17	20	22	25
16	2041	2068	2095	2122	2148	2175	2201	2227	2253	2279	3	5	8	11	13	16	18	21	24
17	2304	2330	2355	2380	2405	2430	2455	2480	2504	2529	2	5	7	10	12	15	17	20	22
18	2553	2577	2601	2625	2648	2672	2695	2718	2742	2765	2	5	7	9	12	14	16	19	21
19	2788	2810	2833	2856	2878	2900	2923	2945	2967	2989	2	4	7	9	11	13	16	18	20
20	3010	3032	3054	3075	3096	3118	3139	3160	3181	3201	2	4	6	8	11	13	15	17	19
21	3222	3243	3263	3284	3304	3324	3345	3365	3385	3404	2	4	6	8	10	12	14	16	18
22	3424	3444	3464	3483	3502	3522	3541	2560	3579	3598	2	4	6	8	10	12	14	15	17
23	3617	3636	3655	3674	3692	3711	3729	3747	3766	3784	2	4	6	7	9	11	13	15	17
24	3802	3820	3838	3856	3874	3892	3909	3927	3945	3962	2	4	5	7	9	11	12	14	16
25	3979	3997	4014	4031	4048	4065	4082	4099	4116	4133	2	3	5	7	9	10	12	14	15
26	4150	4166	4183	4200	4216	4232	4249	4265	4281	4298	2	3	5	7	8	10	11	13	15
27	4314	4330	4346	4362	4378	4393	4409	4425	4440	4456	2	3	5	6	8	9	11	13	14
28	4472	4487	4502	[illegible]	[illegible]	4548	4564	4579	4594	4609	2	3	5	[illegible]	[illegible]	9	11	12	14
29	4624	4639	4654	[illegible]	[illegible]	4698	4713	4728	4742	4757	1	3	4	6	7	9	10	12	13
30	4771	4786	4800	4814	4829	4843	4857	4871	4886	4900	1	3	4	6	7	9	10	11	13

4378 + 8 = 4386

Therefore;

The answer to log of numbers less than 1 will be given in two forms for clarification.

- *Bar notation form*
- *Calculator's result.*

$$for\ bar\ notation\ \mathbf{log}\,0.02745 = \mathbf{\overline{2}.4386}$$

$$Calculator's\ result\ \mathbf{log}\,0.02745 = \mathbf{0.4386 - 2 = -1.5614}$$

$$\mathbf{log\,0.}02745 = \mathbf{\overline{2}.4386}\ \boldsymbol{or} - \mathbf{1.5614}$$

Question 3: ***Evaluate* $\mathbf{0.7345}$ *using logarithm table.***

Solution

To find $\mathbf{log}\,0.7345$*, write the number in standard form.*

$$\mathbf{0.7345} = 7.345 \times 10^{-\mathbf{1}}$$

$$\mathbf{log}\,0.7345 = \log(7.345 \times 10^{-\mathbf{1}})$$

$$\mathbf{log}\,0.7345 = \log 7.345 + \log 10^{-\mathbf{1}}$$

$$\mathbf{log}\,0.7345 = \log 7.345 - 1$$

The power of $\mathbf{10}$ *which is* $-\mathbf{1}$ *is called* ***the Integer or characteristics.***

The ***decimal fraction*** *or* ***mantissa*** *is determined in the Logarithm table.*

From the logarithm table find $\mathbf{73}$ *under* $\mathbf{4}$*, then add mean difference of* $\mathbf{5}$ *as shown below.*

Check the logarithm table at the later-end pages of the book

$\mathbf{73}\ under\ 4 \rightarrow 8657$

$Mean\ difference\ of\ 5 \rightarrow 3$

$$8657 + 3 = 8660$$

Therefore;

The answer to log of numbers less than 1 will be given in two forms for clarification.

- *Bar notation form*
- *Calculator's result.*

$$for\ bar\ notation\ \mathbf{log}\,0.7345 = \mathbf{\bar{1}.8660}$$

$$Calculator's\ result\ \mathbf{log}\,0.7345 = \mathbf{0.8660 - 1} = \mathbf{-0.1340}$$

$$\mathbf{log\,0}.7345 = \mathbf{\bar{1}.8660}\ \boldsymbol{or} - \mathbf{0.1340}$$

Question 4: ***Evaluate* $\mathbf{0.003458}$ *using logarithm table.***

Solution

To find $\mathbf{log}\,0.003458$, *write the number in standard form.*

$$\mathbf{0.003458} = 3.458 \times 10^{-3}$$

$$\mathbf{log}\,0.003458 = \log(3.458 \times 10^{-3})$$

$$\mathbf{log}\,0.003458 = \log 3.458 + \log 10^{-3}$$

$$\mathbf{log}\,0.003458 = \log 3.458 - 3$$

The power of $\mathbf{10}$ *which is* $-\mathbf{3}$ *is called* ***the Integer or characteristics.***

The ***decimal fraction*** *or* ***mantissa*** *is determined in the Logarithm table.*

From the logarithm table find $\mathbf{34}$ *under* $\mathbf{5}$, *then add mean difference of* $\mathbf{8}$ *as shown below.*

Check the logarithm table at the later-end pages of the book

$\mathbf{34}\ under\ 5 \rightarrow \mathbf{5378}$

$Mean\ difference\ of\ 8 \rightarrow \mathbf{10}$

$$\mathbf{5378} \; + \qquad\qquad \mathbf{10} \; = \mathbf{5388}$$

Therefore;

The answer to log of numbers less than 1 will be given in two forms for clarification.

- *Bar notation form*
- *Calculator's result.*

$$for\ bar\ notation\ \mathbf{log}\, 0.003458 = \mathbf{\bar{3}.5388}$$

$$Calculator's\ result\ \mathbf{log}\, 0.7345 = \mathbf{0.5388 - 3 = -2.4612}$$

$$\mathbf{log\, 0}.7345 = \mathbf{\bar{3}.5388}\ \boldsymbol{or} - \mathbf{2.4612}$$

Question 5: ***Evaluate*** $\mathbf{0.08692}$ ***using logarithm table.***

Solution

To find $\mathbf{log}\, 0.08692$*, write the number in standard form.*

$$\mathbf{0.08692} = 8.692 \times 10^{-2}$$

$$\mathbf{log}\, 0.08692 = \log(8.692 \times 10^{-2})$$

$$\mathbf{log}\, 0.08692 = \log 8.692 + \log 10^{-2}$$

$$\mathbf{log}\, 0.08692 = \log 8.692 - 2$$

The power of $\mathbf{10}$ *which is* $-\mathbf{2}$ *is called* ***the Integer or characteristics.***

The ***decimal fraction*** *or* ***mantissa*** *is determined in the Logarithm table.*

From the logarithm table find $\mathbf{86}$ *under* $\mathbf{9}$*, then add mean difference of* $\mathbf{2}$ *as shown below.*

Check the logarithm table at the later-end pages of the book

$\mathbf{86}\ under\ 9 \rightarrow \mathbf{9390}$

$Mean\ difference\ of\ 2 \rightarrow \mathbf{1}$

$\mathbf{9390}$ + $\mathbf{1}$ = **9391**

Therefore;

The answer to log of numbers less than 1 will be given in two forms for clarification.

- *Bar notation form*
- *Calculator's result.*

$$for\ bar\ notation\ \mathbf{log}\, 0.08692 = \mathbf{\bar{2}.9391}$$

$$Calculator's\ result\ \mathbf{log}\, 0.08692 = \mathbf{0.9391 - 2 = -1.0609}$$

$$\mathbf{log\, 0.}08692 = \mathbf{\bar{2}.9391}\ \boldsymbol{or} - \mathbf{1.0609}$$

Question 6: ***Evaluate $\mathbf{0.0007845}$ using logarithm table.***

Solution

To find $\mathbf{log}\, 0.0007845$, *write the number in standard form.*

$$\mathbf{0.0007845} = 7.845 \times 10^{-4}$$

$$\mathbf{log}\, 0.007845 = \log(7.845 \times 10^{-4})$$

$$\mathbf{log}\, 0.007845 = \log 7.845 + \log 10^{-4}$$

$$\mathbf{log}\, 0.007845 = \log 7.845 - 4$$

The power of $\mathbf{10}$ *which is* $-\mathbf{4}$ *is called* ***the Integer or characteristics.***

The ***decimal fraction*** *or* ***mantissa*** *is determined in the Logarithm table.*

From the logarithm table find **78** *under* **4***, then add mean difference of* **5** *as shown below.*

Check the logarithm table at the later-end pages of the book

$\mathbf{78}\ under\ 4 \rightarrow \mathbf{8943}$

$Mean\ difference\ of\ 5 \rightarrow \mathbf{3}$

$$\mathbf{8943}\ + \qquad \mathbf{3} \quad = \mathbf{8946}$$

Therefore;

The answer to log of numbers less than 1 will be given in two forms for clarification.

- *Bar notation form*
- *Calculator's result.*

$$for\ bar\ notation\ \mathbf{log}\, 0.0007845 = \mathbf{\bar{4}.8946}$$

$$Calculator's\ result\ \mathbf{log}\, 0.0007845 = \mathbf{0.8946 - 4 = -3.1054}$$

$$\mathbf{log\, 0.}0007845 = \mathbf{\bar{4}.8946}\ \boldsymbol{or} - \mathbf{3.1054}$$

Unit 6

LOGARITHMS OF NUMBERS LESS THAN 1 – BAR NOTATION ANALYSIS

From the examples of log of numbers greater than 1, the result decreases as the decimal point of the number shifts backward. For example;

Number	Logarithm
2745	3.4393
274.5	2.4393
27.45	1.4393
2.745	0.4393

From the table above, you will observe that, as the decimal point moves backward, the integer or characteristic of the log of number decreases.

Suppose the decimal point moves backward till the number becomes less than 1, such as 0.2745, then the log of 0.2745 will be negative as illustrated below.

$$\log 0.2745 = \log(2.745 \times 10^{-1})$$

$$\mathbf{log}\, 0.2745 = \log 2.745 + \log 10^{-\mathbf{1}}$$

$$\mathbf{log}\, 0.2745 = \log 2.745 - 1$$

$$\mathbf{log}\, 0.2745 = 0.4393 - 1$$

$$\mathbf{log}\, 0.2745 = -1 + 0.4393$$

Also;

$$\log 0.02745 = \log(2.745 \times 10^{-2})$$

$$\mathbf{log}\, 0.2745 = \log 2.745 + \log 10^{-\mathbf{2}}$$

$$\log 0.2745 = \log 2.745 - 2$$

$$\log 0.2745 = 0.4393 - 2$$

$$\log 0.2745 = -2 + 0.4393$$

At this stage, we can have two forms of answers;

- *Calculator's Answer:*

$$= -2 + 0.4383$$

$$= \mathbf{-1.5614}$$

- *Bar Notation:*

$$= -2 + 0.4383$$

$$= \mathbf{\bar{2}.4383}$$

Generally, for logarithm of numbers less than 1, Bar notation result are used.

Therefore; logarithm of 2.745×10^{-n} is is $\mathbf{\bar{n}.4383.}$

The notation $\bar{n}.4383$ implies the combination of a negative integer or characteristics and a positive mantissa.

When it comes to finding the root of a nth of a number, logarithm number with a negative integer and positive mantissa may be challenging.

When finding the root of a number, we take the logarithm of the number, and then divide by it n (the root of the number). If the number is less than 1 and the negative characteristics is not divible by the divisor, the negative characteristics has to be adjusted in a way, to be divisible by the divisor because the negative remainder cannot be carried over to a positive mantissa.

Question 1: ***Simplify*** $\mathbf{\bar{2}.4383 \div 3}$

Solution

$$\frac{\mathbf{\bar{2}.4383}}{\mathbf{3}} = \frac{\bar{2} + 0.4383}{3}$$

Factors of $\bar{2}$ *that will make it divisible by* $3 = \bar{3} + 1$

Substitute $\bar{3} + 1$ *for* $\bar{2}$

$$= \frac{\bar{2} + 0.4383}{3} = \frac{\bar{3} + 1 + 0.4383}{3}$$

$$= \frac{\bar{3} + 1 + 0.4383}{3} = \frac{\bar{3} + 1.4383}{3}$$

$$= \frac{\bar{3} + 1.4383}{3} = \frac{\bar{3}}{3} + \frac{1.4383}{3}$$

$$= \frac{\bar{3}}{3} + \frac{1.4383}{3} = \bar{1} + 0.4794 = \mathbf{\bar{1}.4794}$$

Question 2: ***Simplify*** $\mathbf{\bar{1}.3982 \div 2}$

Solution

$$\frac{\mathbf{\bar{1}.3982}}{\mathbf{2}} = \frac{\bar{1} + 0.3982}{2}$$

Factors of $\bar{1}$ *that will make it divisible by* $2 = \bar{2} + 1$

Substitute $\bar{2} + 1$*for* $\bar{1}$

$$= \frac{\bar{1} + 0.3982}{2} = \frac{\bar{2} + 1 + 0.3982}{2}$$

$$= \frac{\bar{2} + 1 + 0.3982}{2} = \frac{\bar{2} + 1.3982}{2}$$

$$= \frac{\bar{2} + 1.3982}{2} = \frac{\bar{2}}{2} + \frac{1.3982}{2}$$

$$= \frac{\bar{2}}{2} + \frac{1.3982}{2} = \bar{1} + 0.6991 = \mathbf{\bar{1}.6991}$$

Question 3: ***Simplify*** $\mathbf{\bar{2}.5543 \div 5}$

Solution

$$\frac{\bar{2}.5543}{\mathbf{5}} = \frac{\bar{2} + 0.5543}{5}$$

Factors of $\bar{2}$ *that will make it divisible by* $5 = \bar{5} + 3$

Substitute $\bar{5} + 3$*for* $\bar{2}$

$$= \frac{\bar{2} + 0.5543}{5} = \frac{\bar{5} + 3 + 0.5543}{5}$$

$$= \frac{\bar{5} + 3 + 0.5543}{5} = \frac{\bar{5} + 3.5543}{5}$$

$$= \frac{\bar{5} + 3.5543}{5} = \frac{\bar{5}}{5} + \frac{3.5543}{5}$$

$$= \frac{\bar{5}}{5} + \frac{3.5543}{5} = \bar{1} + 0.7109 = \mathbf{\bar{1}.7109}$$

Question 4: ***Simplify*** $\mathbf{\bar{7}.4361 \div 3}$

Solution

$$\frac{\bar{7}.4361}{\mathbf{3}} = \frac{\bar{7} + 0.4361}{3}$$

Factors of $\bar{7}$ *that will make it divisible by* $3 = \bar{9} + 2$

Substitute $\bar{9}+2$*for* $\bar{7}$

$$=\frac{\bar{7}+0.4361}{3}=\frac{\bar{9}+2+0.4361}{3}$$

$$=\frac{\bar{9}+2+0.4361}{3}=\frac{\bar{9}+2.4361}{3}$$

$$=\frac{\bar{9}+2.4361}{3}=\frac{\bar{9}}{3}+\frac{2.4361}{3}$$

$$=\frac{\bar{9}}{3}+\frac{2.4361}{3}=\ \bar{2}+0.8120=\mathbf{\bar{2}.8120}$$

Question 5: ***Simplify*** $\mathbf{\bar{5}.6248 \div 4}$

Solution

$$\frac{\bar{5}.6248}{4}=\frac{\bar{5}+0.6248}{4}$$

Factors of $\bar{5}$ *that will make it divisible by* $4=\bar{8}+3$

Substitute $\bar{8}+3$*for* $\bar{5}$

$$=\frac{\bar{5}+0.6248}{4}=\frac{\bar{8}+3+0.6248}{4}$$

$$=\frac{\bar{8}+5+0.6248}{4}=\frac{\bar{8}+3.6248}{4}$$

$$=\frac{\bar{8}+5.6248}{4}=\frac{\bar{8}}{4}+\frac{3.6248}{4}$$

$$=\frac{\bar{8}}{4}+\frac{3.6248}{4}=\ \bar{2}+0.9062=\mathbf{\bar{2}.9062}$$

Unit 7

ANTILOGARITHM

Antilogarithm is the number for which a given logarithm stands.

For Example;

If $\log x = y$

Antilogarithm of $y = x$**.**

How do you find the antilog of a number?

To find the Antilog of a number, the **characteristics (Integer)** and the **mantissa (fractional part)** are considered.

Question 1 : Use the antilogarithm table to find the antilog of **0.4386**

Solution

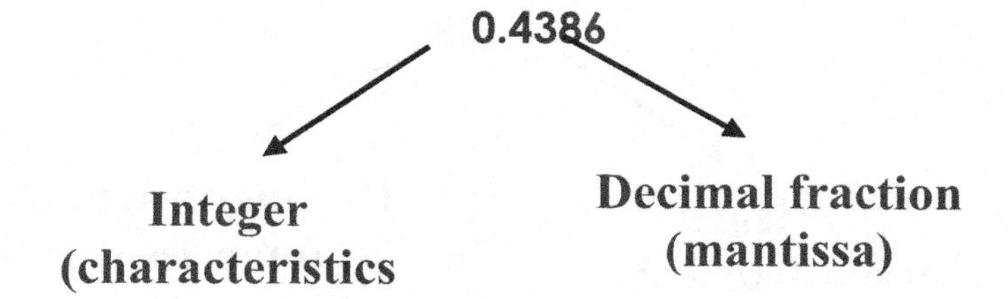

*Use the **Mantissa** to get the antilog value from the Antilogarithm table.*

*From the Antilog Table, check **for 43** under **8**, then add the mean difference of 6 as explained below.*

Antilogarithm Table

	MathsCode										Mean Differences								
	0	1	2	3	4	5	6	7	8	9	1	2	3	4	5	6	7	8	9
.00	1002	1005	1007	1009	1012	1014	1016	1019	1021	0000	0	0	1	1	1	[illegible]	2	2	2
.01	1023	1026	1028	1030	1033	1035	1038	1040	1042	1045	0	0	1	1	1	[illegible]	2	2	2
.02	1047	1050	1052	1054	1057	1059	1062	1064	1067	1069	0	0	1	1	1	[illegible]	2	2	2
⋮							⋮												⋮
.42	2630	2636	2642	2649	2655	2661	2667	2673	2679	2685	1	1	2	2	3	4	4	5	6
.43	2692	2698	2704	2710	2716	2723	2729	2735	2742	2748	1	1	2	3	3	[illegible]	4	5	6
.44	2754	2761	2767	2773	2780	2786	2793	2799	2805	2812	1	1	2	3	3	4	4	5	6

2742 + 4 = 2746

Therefore,

$$\textit{Antilog of } \mathbf{0.4386} = \mathbf{2.746} \times \mathbf{10^0}$$

Integer or characteristics

Value from antilog table using the **mantissa** (4386)

$$= \mathbf{2.746}$$

Question **2:** Use the antilogarithm table to find the antilog of **1.4386**

Solution

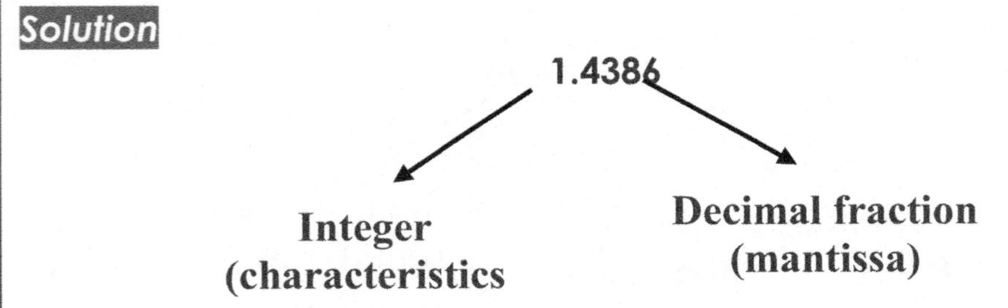

*Use the **Mantissa** to get the antilog value from the Antilogarithm table.*

*From the Antilog Table, check **for 43** under **8,** then add the mean difference of 6 as explained below.*

Antilogarithm Table																			
	MathsCode										Mean Differences								
	0	1	2	3	4	5	6	7	8	9	1	2	3	4	5	6	7	8	9
.00	1002	1005	1007	1009	1012	1014	1016	1019	1021	0000	0	0	1	1	1	1	2	2	2
.01	1023	1026	1028	1030	1033	1035	1038	1040	1042	1045	0	0	1	1	1	1	2	2	2
.02	1047	1050	1052	1054	1057	1059	1062	1064	1067	1069	0	0	1	1	1	1	2	2	2
⋮							⋮												⋮
.42	2630	2636	2642	2649	2655	2661	2667	2673	2679	2685	1	1	2	2	3	4	4	5	6
.43	2692	2698	2704	2710	2716	2723	2729	2735	2742	2748	1	1	2	3	3	4	4	5	6
.44	2754	2761	2767	2773	2780	2786	2793	2799	2805	2812	1	1	2	3	3	4	4	5	6

2742 + 4 = 2746

Therefore,

$$Antilog\ of\ \mathbf{1.4386} = \mathbf{2.746} \times \mathbf{10^1}$$

Integer or characteristics

Value from antilog table using the **mantissa** (4386)

$$= \mathbf{2.746 \times 10 = 27.46}$$

Question 3: Use the antilogarithm table to find the antilog of **2.4386**

Solution

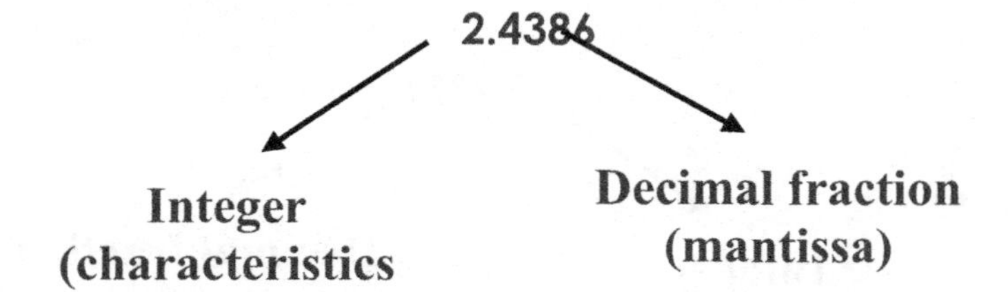

*Use the **Mantissa** to get the antilog value from the Antilogarithm table.*

*From the Antilog Table, check **for 43** under **8,** then add the mean difference of 6 as explained below.*

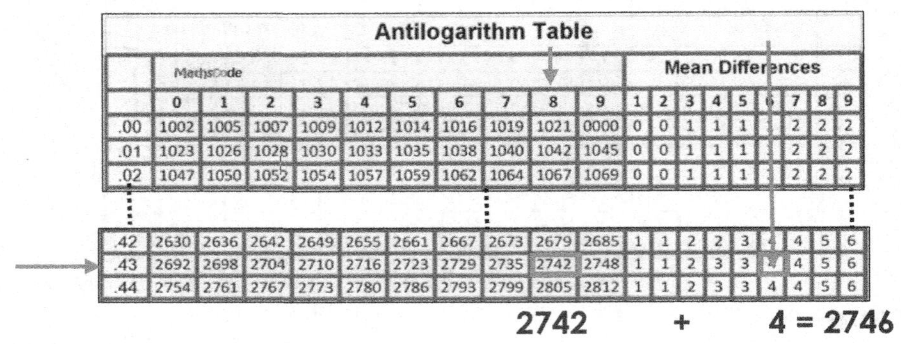

Antilogarithm Table

	0	1	2	3	4	5	6	7	8	9	1	2	3	4	5	6	7	8	9
.00	1002	1005	1007	1009	1012	1014	1016	1019	1021	0000	0	0	1	1	1	1	2	2	2
.01	1023	1026	1028	1030	1033	1035	1038	1040	1042	1045	0	0	1	1	1	1	2	2	2
.02	1047	1050	1052	1054	1057	1059	1062	1064	1067	1069	0	0	1	1	1	1	2	2	2
.42	2630	2636	2642	2649	2655	2661	2667	2673	2679	2685	1	1	2	2	3	4	4	5	6
.43	2692	2698	2704	2710	2716	2723	2729	2735	2742	2748	1	1	2	3	3	4	4	5	6
.44	2754	2761	2767	2773	2780	2786	2793	2799	2805	2812	1	1	2	3	3	4	4	5	6

Therefore,

$$Antilog\ of\ \mathbf{2.4386} = \mathbf{2.746} \times \mathbf{10^2}$$

Integer or characteristics

Value from antilog table using the **mantissa** (4386)

$$= \mathbf{2.746} \times \mathbf{100} = \mathbf{274.6}$$

Question 4: Use the antilogarithm table to find the antilog of **3.4386**

Solutio

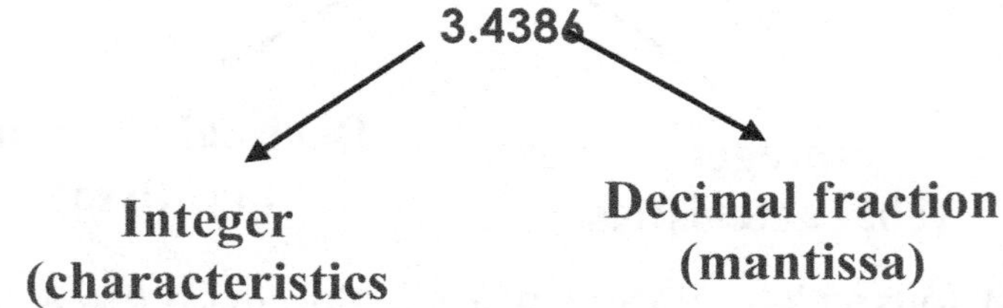

*Use the **Mantissa** to get the antilog value from the Antilogarithm table.*

*From the Antilog Table, check **for 43** under **8,** then add the mean difference of 6 as explained below.*

Antilogarithm Table																		
	MathsCode										Mean Differences							
	0	1	2	3	4	5	6	7	8	9	1	2	3	4	5	6	7	8	9
.00	1002	1005	1007	1009	1012	1014	1016	1019	1021	0000	0	0	1	1	1	[illegible]	2	2	2
.01	1023	1026	1028	1030	1033	1035	1038	1040	1042	1045	0	0	1	1	1	[illegible]	2	2	2
.02	1047	1050	1052	1054	1057	1059	1062	1064	1067	1069	0	0	1	1	1	[illegible]	2	2	2
⋮								⋮											⋮
.42	2630	2636	2642	2649	2655	2661	2667	2673	2679	2685	1	1	2	2	3	4	4	5	6
.43	2692	2698	2704	2710	2716	2723	2729	2735	2742	2748	1	1	2	3	3	4	4	5	6
.44	2754	2761	2767	2773	2780	2786	2793	2799	2805	2812	1	1	2	3	3	4	4	5	6

2742 + 4 = 2746

Therefore,

$$Antilog\ of\ \mathbf{3.4386 = 2.746 \times 10^3}$$

Integer or characteristics

Value from antilog table using the **mantissa** (4386)

$$\mathbf{= 2.746 \times 1000 = 2746}$$

Question 5: Use the antilogarithm table to find the antilog of $\mathbf{\bar{1}.4386}$

Solution

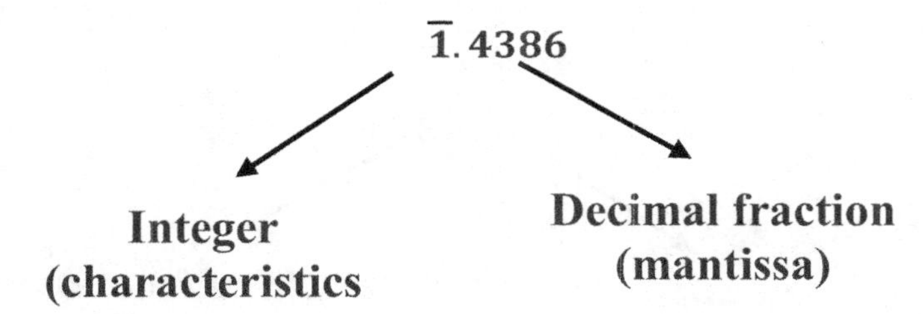

*Use the **Mantissa** to get the antilog value from the Antilogarithm table.*

*From the Antilog Table, check **for 43** under **8,** then add the mean difference of 6 as explained below.*

Antilogarithm Table

	Mathscode										Mean Differences								
	0	1	2	3	4	5	6	7	8	9	1	2	3	4	5	6	7	8	9
.00	1002	1005	1007	1009	1012	1014	1016	1019	1021	0000	0	0	1	1	1	1	2	2	2
.01	1023	1026	1028	1030	1033	1035	1038	1040	1042	1045	0	0	1	1	1	1	2	2	2
.02	1047	1050	1052	1054	1057	1059	1062	1064	1067	1069	0	0	1	1	1	1	2	2	2
⋮							⋮												⋮
.42	2630	2636	2642	2649	2655	2661	2667	2673	2679	2685	1	1	2	2	3	4	4	5	6
.43	2692	2698	2704	2710	2716	2723	2729	2735	2742	2748	1	1	2	3	3	4	4	5	6
.44	2754	2761	2767	2773	2780	2786	2793	2799	2805	2812	1	1	2	3	3	4	4	5	6

2742 + 4 = 2746

Therefore,

$$Antilog\ of\ \bar{\mathbf{1}}.\mathbf{4386} = \mathbf{2.746} \times \mathbf{10^{-1}}$$

Integer or characteristics

Value from antilog table using the **mantissa** (4386)

$$= \mathbf{2.746 \times 0.1 = 0.2746}$$

Question 6: Use the antilogarithm table to find the antilog of $\bar{\mathbf{2}}.\mathbf{4386}$

Solution

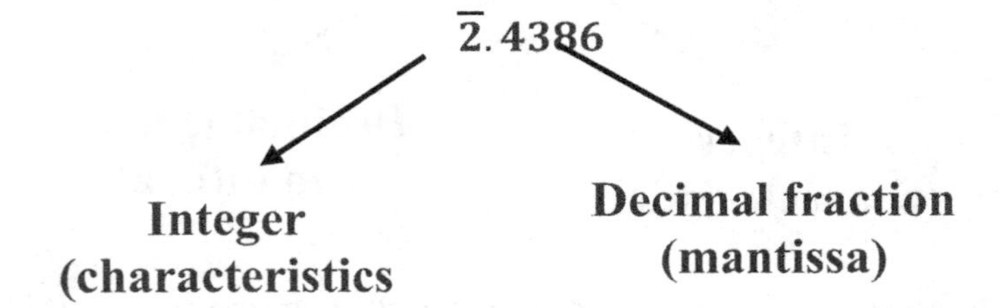

*Use the **Mantissa** to get the antilog value from the Antilogarithm table.*

*From the Antilog Table, check **for 43** under **8,** then add the mean difference of 6 as explained below.*

Antilogarithm Table

	MathsCode										Mean Differences								
	0	1	2	3	4	5	6	7	8	9	1	2	3	4	5	6	7	8	9
.00	1002	1005	1007	1009	1012	1014	1016	1019	1021	0000	0	0	1	1	1	1	2	2	2
.01	1023	1026	1028	1030	1033	1035	1038	1040	1042	1045	0	0	1	1	1	1	2	2	2
.02	1047	1050	1052	1054	1057	1059	1062	1064	1067	1069	0	0	1	1	1	1	2	2	2
⋮							⋮												⋮
.42	2630	2636	2642	2649	2655	2661	2667	2673	2679	2685	1	1	2	2	3	4	4	5	6
.43	2692	2698	2704	2710	2716	2723	2729	2735	2742	2748	1	1	2	3	3	[illegible]	4	5	6
.44	2754	2761	2767	2773	2780	2786	2793	2799	2805	2812	1	1	2	3	3	4	4	5	6

2742 + 4 = 2746

Therefore,

$$Antilog\ of\, \overline{\mathbf{2}}.\mathbf{4386} \ = \mathbf{2.746} \times \mathbf{10^{-2}}$$

Integer or characteristics

Value from antilog table using the **mantissa** (4386)

$$= \mathbf{2.746 \times 0.01 = 0.02746}$$

Summarily, from question 31 to 34

Anti $\mathbf{log\ of\ \overline{2}.4386 = 0.02746}$

Anti $\mathbf{log\ of\ \overline{1}.4386 = 0.2746}$

Anti $\mathbf{log\ of\ 0.4386 = 2.746}$

Anti $\mathbf{log\ of\ 1.4386 = 27.46}$

Anti $\mathbf{log\ of\ 2.4386 = 274.6}$

Anti $\mathbf{log\ of\ 3.4386 = 2746}$

As the value of **integer or characteristics** increases. the decimal point moves forward.

Question 7: Use the antilogarithm table to find the antilog of **3.0363**

Solution

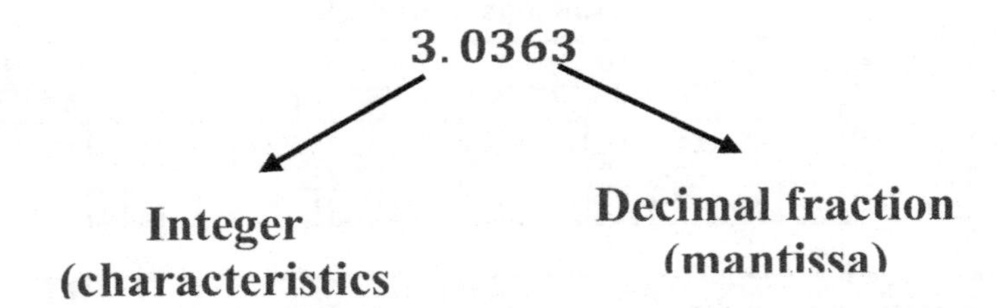

*Use the **Mantissa** to get the antilog value from the Antilogarithm table.*

*From the Antilog Table, check **for** $\mathbf{.03}$ under $\mathbf{6}$**,** then add the mean difference of 3 as explained below.*

Check the Anti logarithm table at the later-end pages of the book

$.\mathbf{03}\ under\ 6 \rightarrow \mathbf{1086}$

$Mean\ difference\ of\ 3 \rightarrow \mathbf{1}$

1086 + 1 = 1087

Therefore,

$$Antilog\ of \mathbf{3.0363}\ = \mathbf{1.087}\ \times \mathbf{10^3}$$

Integer or characteristics

Value from antilog table using the **mantissa** (4386)

$$= \mathbf{1.087 \times 1000 = 1087}$$

Question 8: Use the antilogarithm table to find the antilog of **5.7076**

Solution

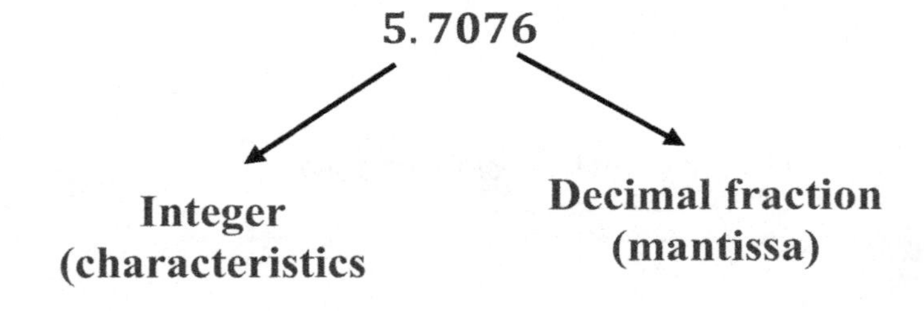

Use the ***Mantissa*** to get the antilog value from the Antilogarithm table.

From the Antilog Table, check ***for*** $.\mathbf{70}$ *under* **7**, *then add the mean difference of 6 as explained below.*

Check the Anti-logarithm table at the later-end pages of the book

$.\mathbf{70}\ under\ 7 \rightarrow \mathbf{5093}$

$Mean\ difference\ of\ 3 \rightarrow \mathbf{7}$

Therefore, **5093 + 7 = 6100**

$$Antilog\ of\ \mathbf{5.7076} = \mathbf{6.100} \times \mathbf{10^5}$$

Integer or characteristics

Value from antilog table using the **mantissa** (4386)

$$= \mathbf{6.100 \times 100000 = 6100000}$$

Question 9: Use the antilogarithm table to find the antilog of $\mathbf{\bar{1}.5980}$

Solution

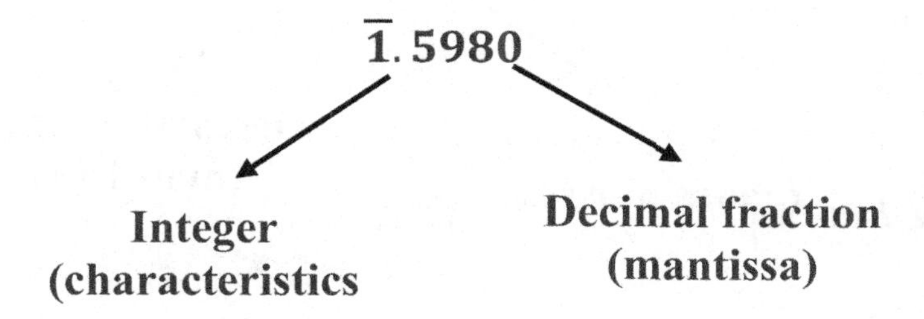

Use the ***Mantissa*** to get the antilog value from the Antilogarithm table.

From the Antilog Table, check **for** $.59$ *under* $\mathbf{8}$, *then add the mean difference of* 0 *as explained below.*

Check the Anti-logarithm table at the later-end pages of the book

$.\mathbf{59}\ under\ 8 \rightarrow \mathbf{3963}$

$Mean\ difference\ of\ 0 \rightarrow \mathbf{0}$

3963 + 0 = 3963

Therefore,

$$Antilog\ of\ \bar{\mathbf{1}}.\mathbf{5980} = \mathbf{3.963} \times \mathbf{10^{-1}}$$

Integer or characteristics

Value from antilog table using the **mantissa** (4386)

$$= \mathbf{3.963 \times 0.1 = 0.3963}$$

Question 10:: Use the antilogarithm table to find the antilog of $\bar{\mathbf{2}}.\mathbf{7952}$

Solution

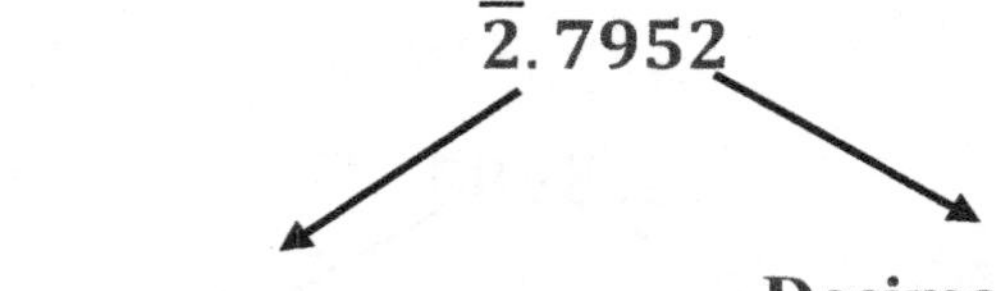

Use the **Ma** ... *tilog value from the Antilogarithm table.*

From the Antilog Table, check **for** $.79$ *under* $\mathbf{5}$, *then add the mean difference of* 2 *as explained below.*

Check the Anti-logarithm table at the later-end pages of the book

$.\mathbf{59}\ under\ 8 \rightarrow \mathbf{6237}$

$Mean\ difference\ of\ 0 \rightarrow \mathbf{3}$

6237 + 3 = 6240

Therefore,

$$Antilog\ of\ \bar{\mathbf{2}}.\mathbf{7952} = \mathbf{6.240} \times \mathbf{10^{-2}}$$

Integer or characteristics

Value from antilog table using the **mantissa** (4386)

$$= \mathbf{6.240 \times 0.01 = 0.06240}$$

Unit 8

OPERATIONS ON COMMON LOGARITHMS

MULTIPLICATION OF NUMBERS GREATER THAN 1

How can you use logarithm table to multiply numbers?

Steps:

1. Express the numbers as logarithm, that is find the logarithm value of the numbers.
2. Add the logarithm values of all the numbers given.
3. Find the Antilog of the total value.

Question 1: Multiply **12.34 and 139.7**

Solution

find the logarithm value of the numbers

Number	Standard Form	Logarithm Value
12.34	1.234×10^1	1.0912
$\times$		+
139.7	1.397×10^2	2.1453
		3.2365

Add the logarithm values of all the numbers given.

$$\mathbf{1.0912 + 2.1453 = 3.2365}$$

Find the Anti log of the total value.

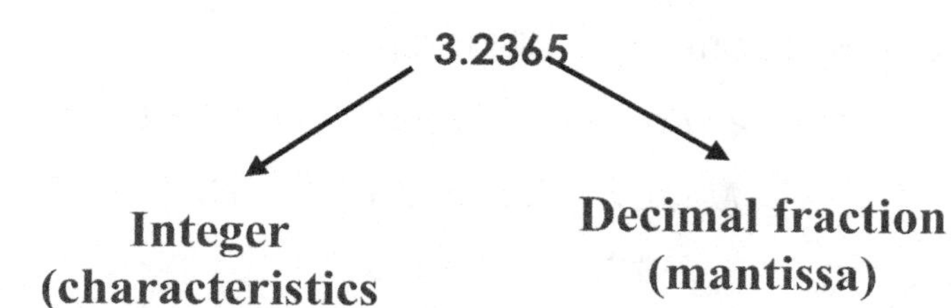

Check the Antilogarithm table for:

$$The\ value\ of\ \mathbf{23}\ under\ \mathbf{6}\ =\ \mathbf{1722}$$

$$Mean\ difference\ of\ \mathbf{5} = \mathbf{2}$$

$$\mathbf{1722 + 2 = 1724}$$

Therefore,

Antilog of $\mathbf{3.2365 = 1.724 \times 10^3}$

$$\mathbf{= 1724}$$

Question 2: Multiply **2.421 and 304.6**

Solution

find the logarithm value of the numbers

Number	***Standard Form***	***Logarithm Value***
2.421	2.421×10^0	0.3840
$\times$		+
304.6	3.046×10^2	2.4838
		$\mathbf{2.8678}$

Add the logarithm values of all the numbers given.

$$\mathbf{0.3840 + 2.4839 = 2.8678}$$

Find the Anti log of the total value.

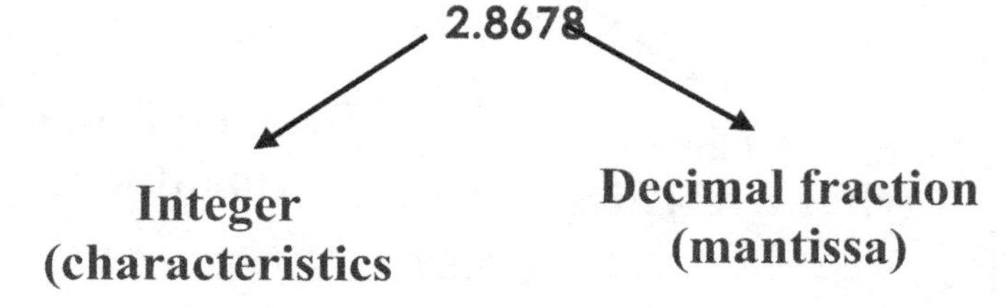

Check the Antilogarithm table for:

$$\text{The value of } \mathbf{86} \text{ under } \mathbf{7} = \mathbf{7362}$$

$$\text{Mean difference of } \mathbf{8} = \mathbf{13}$$

$$\mathbf{7362 + 13 = 7375}$$

Therefore,

Antilog of $\mathbf{2.8678 = 7.375 \times 10^2}$

$$\mathbf{= 737.5}$$

Question 3: Simplify $\mathbf{2.789 \times 14.86 \times 142.8}$ using the logarithm table

Solution

find the logarithm value of the numbers

Number	***Standard Form***	***Logarithm Value***
2.789	2.789×10^0	0.4454
$\times$		+
14.86	1.486×10^1	1.1721
$\times$		+
142.8	1.428×10^2	2.1547
		3.7722

Add the logarithm values of all the numbers given.

$$\mathbf{0.4454 + 1.1721 + 2.1547 = 3.7722}$$

Find the Anti log of the total value.

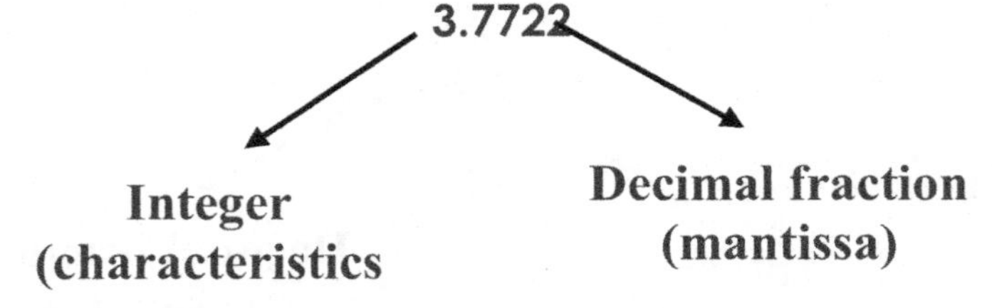

Check the Antilogarithm table for:

$$\text{The value of } \mathbf{77} \text{ under } \mathbf{2} = \mathbf{5916}$$

$$Mean\ difference\ of\ \mathbf{2} = \mathbf{3}$$

$$\mathbf{5916 + 3 = 5919}$$

Therefore,

Antilog of $\mathbf{3.7722 = 5.916 \times 10^3}$

$$= \mathbf{5916}$$

Question 4: Simplify $\mathbf{13.81 \times 37.86}$ using the logarithm table

Solution

find the logarithm value of the numbers

Number	Standard Form	Logarithm Value
13.81 × 37.86	1.381×10^1 3.786×10^1	1.1402 + 1.5783
		2.7185

Add the logarithm values of all the numbers given.

$$\mathbf{1.1402 + 1.5783 = 2.7185}$$

Find the Anti log of the total value.

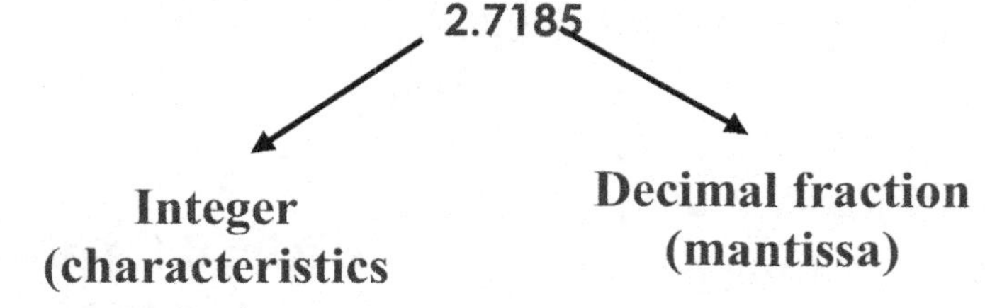

Check the Antilogarithm table for:

$$The\ value\ of\ \mathbf{71}\ under\ \mathbf{8}\ =\ \mathbf{5224}$$

$$Mean\ difference\ of\ \mathbf{5} = \mathbf{6}$$

$$5224 + 6 = 5230$$

Therefore,

Antilog of $\mathbf{2.7185 = 5.230 \times 10^2}$

$$\mathbf{= 523}$$

Question 5: Simplify $\mathbf{14.86 \times 2.789 \times 39.61}$ using the logarithm table

Solution

find the logarithm value of the numbers

Number	Standard Form	Logarithm Value
14.86	1.486×10^1	1.1721
$\times$		+
2.789	2.789×10^0	0.4454
$\times$		+
39.61	1.428×10^1	1.5978
		3.4153

Add the logarithm values of all the numbers given.

$$\mathbf{1.1721 + 0.4454 + 1.5978 = 3.4153}$$

Find the Anti log of the total value.

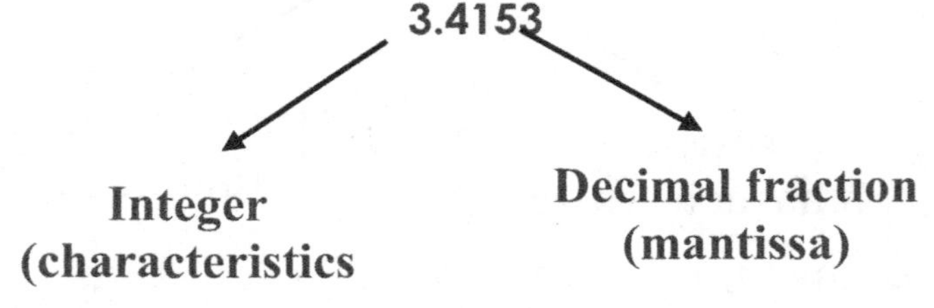

Check the Antilogarithm table for:

$$\textit{The value of } \mathbf{41} \textit{ under } \mathbf{5} = \mathbf{5916}$$

$$\textit{Mean difference of } \mathbf{3 = 3}$$

$$5916 + 3 = 5919$$

Therefore,

Antilog of $3.7722 = 5.916 \times 10^3$

$$= 5916$$

Question 6: Simplify $(20.42)^2$ using the logarithm table

Solution

find the logarithm value of the numbers

Number	Standard Form	Logarithm Value
20.42	2.042×10^1	1.3100
		×
$(20.42)^2$		2
		2.6200

Add the logarithm values of all the numbers given.

$$1.3100 \times 2 = 2.6200$$

Find the Anti log of the total value.

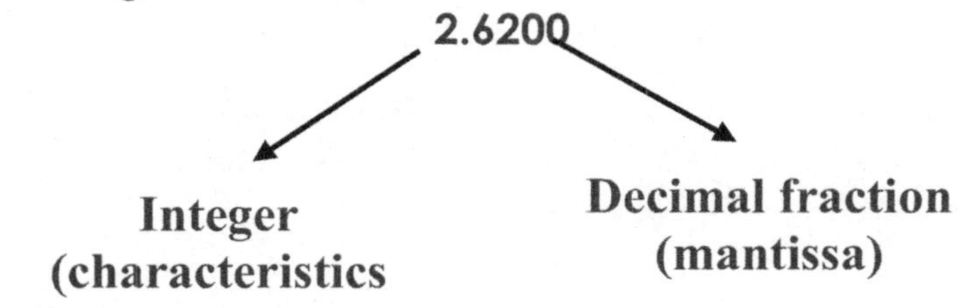

Check the Antilogarithm table for:

$$The\ value\ of\ \mathbf{62}\ under\ \mathbf{0} = \mathbf{4169}$$

$$Mean\ difference\ of\ \mathbf{0} = \mathbf{0}$$

$$4169 + 0 = 4169$$

Therefore,

Antilog of $2.6200 = 4.169 \times 10^2$

$$= 416.9$$

Unit 9

DIVISIONS OF NUMBERS GREATER THAN 1

How can you use logarithm table to divide numbers?

Steps

1. Express the numbers as logarithm, that is find the logarithm value of the numbers.
2. Subtract the logarithm values of the numbers.
3. Find the Antilog of the total value.

Question 1 : **Use the logarithm table to evaluate**

$$87.42 \div 28.79$$

Solution

find the logarithm value of the numbers

Number	***Standard Form***	***Logarithm Value***
87.42	8.742×10^1	1.9416
$\div$		$-$
28.79	2.879×10^1	1.4593
		0.4823

Add the logarithm values of all the numbers given.

$$\mathbf{1.9416 - 1.4593 = 0.4823}$$

Find the Anti log of the total value.

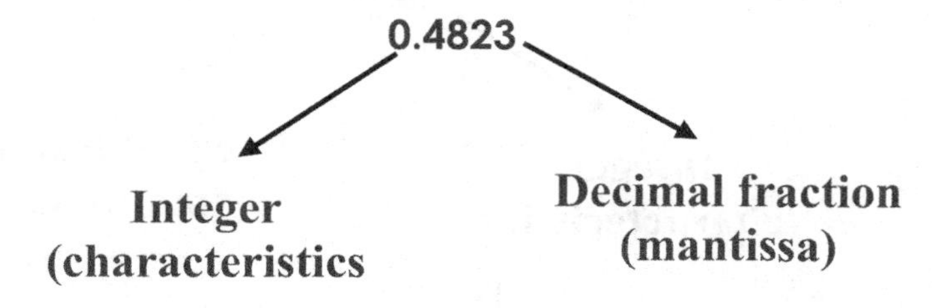

Check the Antilogarithm table for:

$$The\ value\ of\ \mathbf{48}\ under\ \mathbf{2}\ =\ \mathbf{3034}$$

$$Mean\ difference\ of\ \mathbf{3} = \mathbf{2}$$

$$\mathbf{3036 + 2 = 3036}$$

Therefore,

Antilog of $\mathbf{0.4823 = 3.036 \times 10^0}$

$$\mathbf{= 3.036}$$

Question 2 : **Use the logarithm table to evaluate**

$$\mathbf{436.7 \div 20.47}$$

Solution

find the logarithm value of the numbers

Number	***Standard Form***	***Logarithm Value***
436.7	4.367×10^2	2.6402
÷		−
20.47	2.047×10^1	1.3111
		1.3291

Add the logarithm values of all the numbers given.

$$\mathbf{2.6402 - \ 1.3111 = 1.3291}$$

Find the Anti log of the total value.

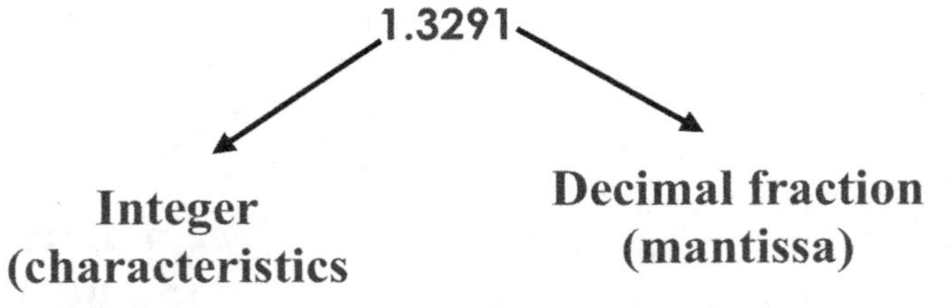

Check the Antilogarithm table for:

$$The\ value\ of\ \mathbf{32}\ under\ \mathbf{9}\ =\ \mathbf{2133}$$

$$Mean\ difference\ of\ \mathbf{1} = \mathbf{0}$$

$$\mathbf{2133 + 0 = 2133}$$

Therefore,

Antilog of $\mathbf{1.3291 = 2.133 \times 10^1}$

$$\mathbf{= 21.33}$$

Question 3: **Use the logarithm table to evaluate** $\mathbf{13.42 \div 2.431}$

Solution

find the logarithm value of the numbers

Number	Standard Form	Logarithm Value
13.42	1.342×10^1	1.1277
÷		−
2.431	2.431×10^0	0.3876
		0.7401

Add the logarithm values of all the numbers given.

$$\mathbf{1.1277 - 0.3876 = 0.7401}$$

Find the Anti log of the total value.

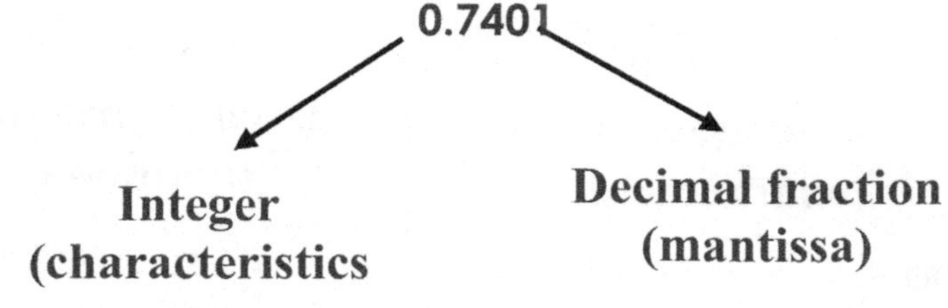

Check the Antilogarithm table for:

$$The\ value\ of\ \mathbf{74}\ under\ \mathbf{0}\ =\ \mathbf{5494}$$

$$Mean\ difference\ of\ \mathbf{1} = \mathbf{1}$$

$$\mathbf{5494 + 1 = 5495}$$

Therefore,

Antilog of $\mathbf{0.7401 = 5.495 \times 10^0}$

$$\mathbf{= 5.495}$$

Question 4: **Use the logarithm table to evaluate**

$$\mathbf{276.8 \div 14.86}$$

Solution

find the logarithm value of the numbers

Number	Standard Form	Logarithm Value
276.8	2.768×10^2	2.4422
÷		−
14.86	1.486×10^1	1.1721
		1.2701

Add the logarithm values of all the numbers given.

$$\mathbf{2.4422 - 1.1721 = 1.2701}$$

Find the Anti log of the total value.

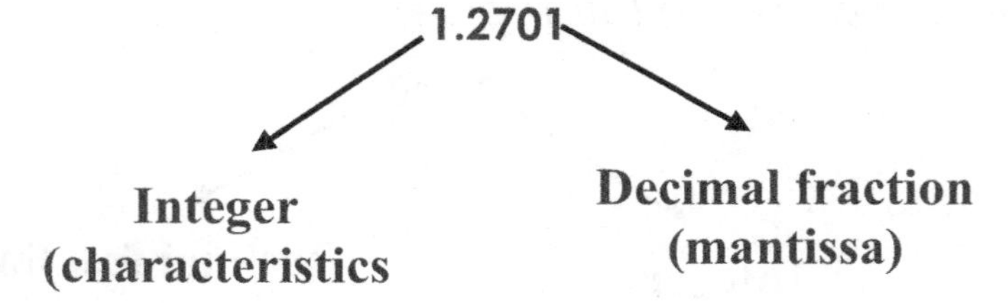

Check the Antilogarithm table for:

$$The\ value\ of\ \mathbf{27}\ under\ \mathbf{0}\ =\ \mathbf{1862}$$

$$Mean\ difference\ of\ \mathbf{1 = 0}$$

$$\mathbf{1862 + 0 = 1862}$$

Therefore,

Antilog of $\mathbf{1.2701 = 1.862 \times 10^1}$

$$\mathbf{= 18.62}$$

Question 5: **Use the logarithm table to evaluate**

$$\mathbf{40.79 \div 15.42}$$

Solution

find the logarithm value of the numbers

Number	***Standard Form***	***Logarithm Value***
40.79	4.079×10^1	1.6106
÷		−
15.42	1.542×10^1	1.1881
		0.4225

Add the logarithm values of all the numbers given.

$$\mathbf{1.7106 - 1.1881 = 0.5325}$$

Find the Anti log of the total value.

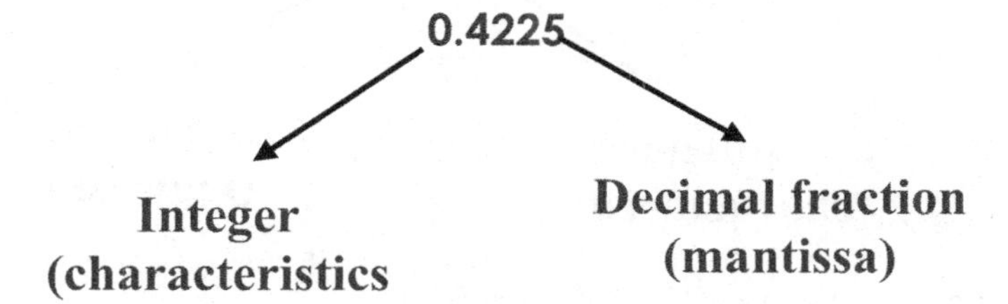

Check the Antilogarithm table for:

$$The\ value\ of\ \mathbf{42}\ under\ \mathbf{2}\ =\ \mathbf{2642}$$

$$Mean\ difference\ of\ \mathbf{5 = 3}$$

$$\mathbf{2642 + 3 = 2645}$$

Therefore,

Antilog of $\mathbf{0.4225 = 2.642 \times 10^0}$

$$\mathbf{= 2.642}$$

Question 6: **Use the logarithm table to evaluate**

$$\mathbf{1.034 \div 24.31}$$

Solution

find the logarithm value of the numbers

Number	*Standard Form*	*Logarithm Value*
1.034	1.034×10^0	0.0145
÷		−
24.31	2.431×10^1	1.3858
		$\mathbf{\bar{2}.6287}$

Add the logarithm values of all the numbers given.

$$\mathbf{0.0145 - 1.3858 = \bar{2}.6287}$$

Find the Anti log of the total value.

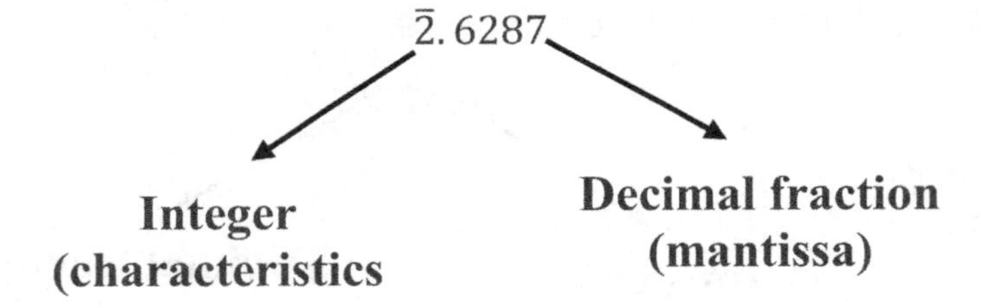

Check the Antilogarithm table for:

$$\textit{The value of } \mathbf{62} \textit{ under } \mathbf{8 = 4246}$$

$$\textit{Mean difference of } \mathbf{7 = 7}$$

$$\mathbf{4246 + 7 = 4253}$$

Therefore,

Antilog of $\mathbf{\bar{2}.6287 = 4.253 \times 10^{-2}}$

$$= 0.04253$$

Unit 10

MULTIPLICATION OF NUMBERS LESS THAN 1

How can you use logarithm table to multiply numbers that are lesser than 1?

Steps

1. Rewrite the number in standard form.
2. Express the coefficient as logarithm, that is find the logarithm value of the coefficient.
3. Sum up the logarithm values of all the coefficients.
4. Find the Antilog of the total value.

Question 1: **Use the logarithm table to** Multiply **0.003458 and 0.8461**

Solution

find the logarithm value of the numbers

Number	***Standard Form***	***Logarithm Value***
0.003458	3.458×10^{-5}	$\bar{3}.5388$
$\times$		$+$
0.8461	8.461×10^{-1}	$\bar{1}.9274$
		$\bar{3}.\mathbf{4662}$

Add the logarithm values of all the numbers given.

$$\bar{3}.5388 + \bar{1}.9274 = \bar{3}.\mathbf{4662}$$

Find the Anti log of the total value.

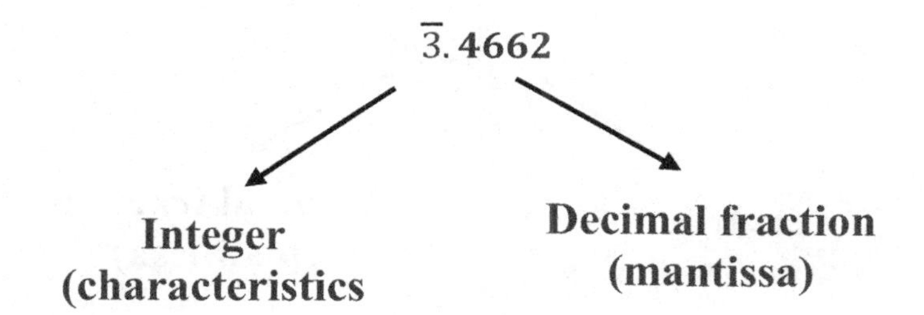

Check the Antilogarithm table for:

$$The\ value\ of\ \mathbf{46}\ under\ \mathbf{6}\ =\ \mathbf{2924}$$

$$Mean\ difference\ of\ \mathbf{2} = \mathbf{1}$$

$$\mathbf{2924 + 1 = 2925}$$

Therefore,

Antilog of $\overline{3}.\mathbf{4662 = 2.925 \times 10^{-3}}$

$$= \mathbf{0.002925}$$

Question 2: **Use the logarithm table to** Multiply $\mathbf{0.296}\ \boldsymbol{and}\ \mathbf{0.0082}$

Solution

find the logarithm value of the numbers

Number	**Standard Form**	**Logarithm Value**
0.296	2.96×10^{-1}	$\overline{1}.4713$
$\times$		$+$
0.0082	8.2×10^{-3}	$\overline{3}.9138$
		$\overline{3}.\mathbf{3851}$

Add the logarithm values of all the numbers given.

$$\overline{1}.4713 + \overline{3}.9138 = \overline{3}.\mathbf{3851}$$

Find the Anti log of the total value.

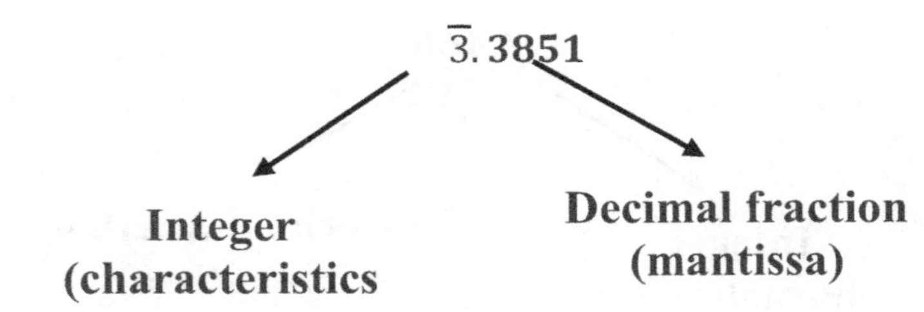

Check the Antilogarithm table for:

$$The\ value\ of\ \mathbf{38}\ under\ \mathbf{5}\ =\ \mathbf{2427}$$

$$Mean\ difference\ of\ \mathbf{1} = \mathbf{1}$$

$$\mathbf{2924 + 1 = 2428}$$

Therefore,

Antilog of $\overline{3}.\mathbf{3851} = \mathbf{2.428 \times 10^{-3}}$

$$= \mathbf{0.002428}$$

Question 3: **Use the logarithm table to** Multiply $\mathbf{0.6735}$ ***and*** $\mathbf{0.3507}$

Solution

find the logarithm value of the numbers

Number	Standard Form	Logarithm Value
0.6735	6.735×10^{-1}	$\overline{1}.8283$
$\times$		$+$
0.3507	3.507×10^{-1}	$\overline{1}.5450$
		$\overline{1}.\mathbf{3733}$

Add the logarithm values of all the numbers given.

$$\overline{1}.8283 + \overline{1}.5450 = \overline{1}.\mathbf{3733}$$

Find the Anti log of the total value.

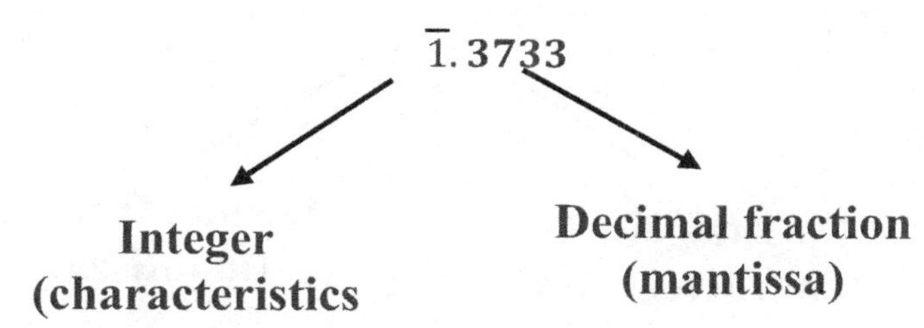

Check the Antilogarithm table for:

$$\textit{The value of } \mathbf{37} \textit{ under } \mathbf{3} = \mathbf{2360}$$

$$\textit{Mean difference of } \mathbf{3} = \mathbf{2}$$

$$\mathbf{2360 + 2 = 2362}$$

Therefore,

Antilog of $\overline{1}.\mathbf{2360} = \mathbf{2.362 \times 10^{-1}}$

$$= \mathbf{0.2362}$$

Question 4: **Use the logarithm table to** Multiply $\mathbf{0.03175} \times \mathbf{0.7642} \times \mathbf{0.928}$

Solution

find the logarithm value of the numbers

Number	Standard Form	Logarithm Value
0.7642	7.642×10^{-1}	$\overline{1}.8832$
$\times$		$+$
0.928	9.28×10^{-1}	$\overline{1}.9675$
		$\overline{1}.\mathbf{8507}$

Add the logarithm values of all the numbers given.

$$\overline{1}.8832 + \overline{1}.9675 = \overline{1}.\mathbf{8507}$$

Find the Anti log of the total value.

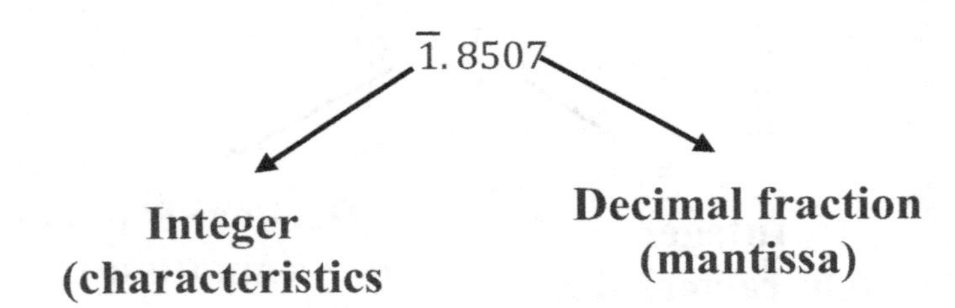

Check the Antilogarithm table for:

$$The\ value\ of\ \mathbf{85}\ under\ \mathbf{0} = \mathbf{9294}$$

$$Mean\ difference\ of\ \mathbf{7} = \mathbf{4}$$

$$\mathbf{9294 + 4 = 9298}$$

Therefore,

Antilog of $\bar{1}.\mathbf{8507} = \mathbf{9.298 \times 10^{-1}}$

$$= \mathbf{0.9298}$$

Question 5: **Use the logarithm table to** Multiply $\mathbf{0.8385} \times \mathbf{0.0678}$

Solution

find the logarithm value of the numbers

Number	Standard Form	Logarithm Value
0.8385 $\times$ 0.0678	8.385×10^{-1} 6.78×10^{-2}	$\bar{1}.9235$ $+$ $\bar{2}.8312$
		$\bar{2}.\mathbf{7547}$

Add the logarithm values of all the numbers given.

$$\bar{1}.9235 + \bar{2}.8312 = \bar{2}.\mathbf{7547}$$

Find the Anti log of the total value.

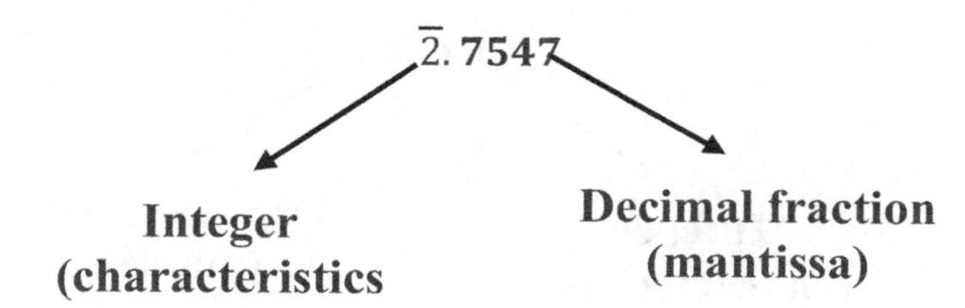

Check the Antilogarithm table for:

$$The\ value\ of\ \mathbf{75}\ under\ \mathbf{4}\ =\ \mathbf{5675}$$

$$Mean\ difference\ of\ \mathbf{7} = 9$$

$$\mathbf{5675 + 7 = 5684}$$

Therefore,

Antilog of $\bar{2}.\mathbf{7547} = \mathbf{5.684 \times 10^{-2}}$

$$= \mathbf{0.05684}$$

> Question 6: **Use the logarithm table to** Multiply $\mathbf{0.925} \times \mathbf{0.09233} \times \mathbf{0.02243}$

Solution

find the logarithm value of the numbers

Number	**Standard Form**	**Logarithm Value**
0.925	9.25×10^{-1}	$\bar{1}.9661$
$\times$		$+$
0.09233	9.233×10^{-2}	$\bar{2}.9653$
$\times$		$+$
0.02243	2.243×10^{-2}	$\bar{2}.3508$
		$\mathbf{\bar{3}.2822}$

Add the logarithm values of all the numbers given.

$$\bar{1}.9661 + \bar{2}.9653 + \bar{2}.\mathbf{3508} = \bar{3}.\mathbf{2822}$$

Find the Anti log of the total value.

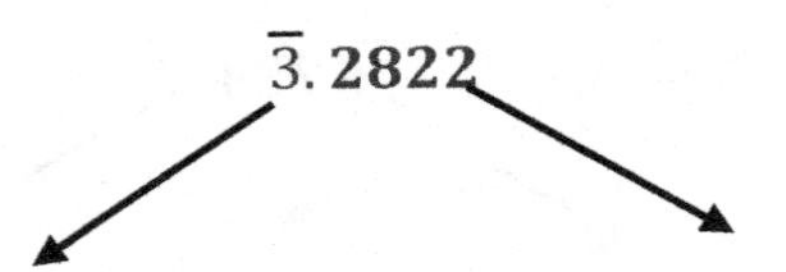

Integer (characteristics

Decimal fraction (mantissa)

Check the Antilogarithm table for:

$$The\ value\ of\ \mathbf{28}\ under\ \mathbf{2}\ = 1914$$

$$Mean\ difference\ of\ \mathbf{2} = \mathbf{1}$$

$$\mathbf{1914 + 1 = 1915}$$

Therefore,

Antilog of $\overline{3}.\mathbf{2822} = \mathbf{1.915 \times 10^{-3}}$

$$= \mathbf{0.001915}$$

Unit 11

DIVISION OF NUMBERS LESS THAN 1

How can you use logarithm table to divide numbers?

Steps

1. Rewrite the number in standard form.
2. Express the coefficient as logarithm, that is find the logarithm value of the coefficient.
3. Subtract up the logarithm values of all the coefficients.
4. Find the Antilog of the total value.

Question 1: **Use the logarithm table to evaluate**

$$\mathbf{0.4826 \div 0.005926}$$

Solution

find the logarithm value of the numbers

Number	Standard Form	Logarithm Value
0.4826	4.826×10^{-1}	$\bar{1}.6835$
$\div$		$-$
0.005926	5.926×10^{-3}	$\bar{3}.7727$
		$1.\mathbf{9108}$

Add the logarithm values of all the numbers given.

$$\bar{1}.6835 - \bar{3}.7727 = 1.\mathbf{9108}$$

Find the Anti log of the total value.

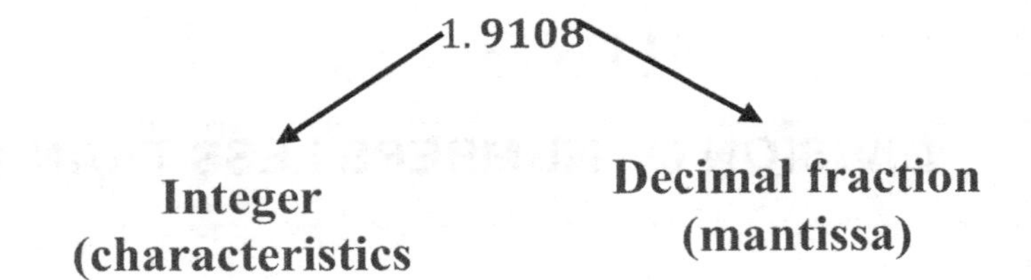

Check the Antilogarithm table for:

$$\textit{The value of } \mathbf{91} \textit{ under } \mathbf{0} = \mathbf{8128}$$

$$\textit{Mean difference of } \mathbf{8} = \mathbf{15}$$

$$\mathbf{8128 + 15 = 8143}$$

Therefore,

Antilog of $\mathbf{1.9108 = 8.143 \times 10^1}$

$$\mathbf{= 81.43}$$

Question 2: **Use the logarithm table to evaluate** $\mathbf{3.925 \div 0.03175}$

Solution

find the logarithm value of the numbers

Number	Standard Form	Logarithm Value
3.925	3.925×10^0	0.5939
$\div$		$-$
0.03175	3.175×10^{-2}	$\bar{2}.5018$
		2.0921

Add the logarithm values of all the numbers given.

$$0.5939 - \bar{2}.5018 = 2.\mathbf{0921}$$

Find the Anti log of the total value.

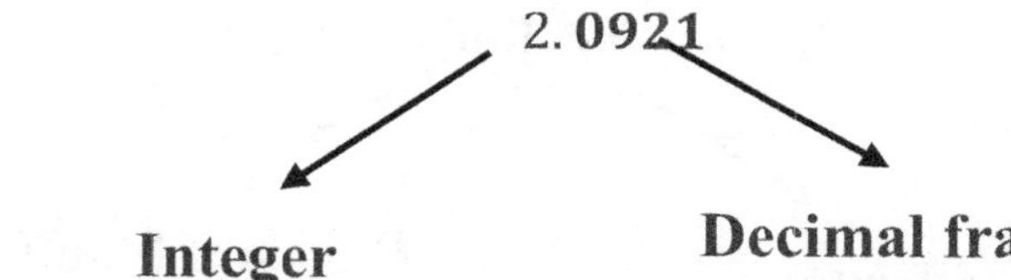

Check the Antilogarithm table for:

$$The\ value\ of\ \mathbf{09}\ under\ \mathbf{2}\ =\ \mathbf{1236}$$

$$Mean\ difference\ of\ \mathbf{1} = \mathbf{0}$$

$$\mathbf{1236 + 0 = 1236}$$

Therefore,

Antilog of $\mathbf{2.0921 = 1.236 \times 10^2}$

$$\mathbf{= 123.6}$$

Question 3: **Use the logarithm table to evaluate** $\mathbf{0.52 \div 0.09235}$

Solution

find the logarithm value of the numbers

Number	***Standard Form***	***Logarithm Value***
0.52	5.2×10^{-1}	$\bar{1}.7160$
$\div$		$-$
0.09235	9.235×10^{-2}	$\bar{2}.9654$
		$\mathbf{0.7506}$

Add the logarithm values of all the numbers given.

$$\bar{1}.7160 - \bar{2}.9654 = 0.\mathbf{7506}$$

Find the Anti log of the total value.

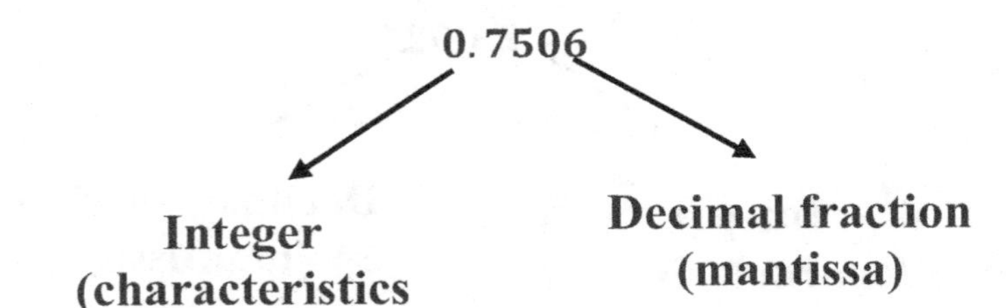

Check the Antilogarithm table for:

$$The\ value\ of\ \mathbf{75}\ under\ \mathbf{0} = 5623$$

$$Mean\ difference\ of\ \mathbf{6 = 8}$$

$$\mathbf{5623 + 8 = 5631}$$

Therefore,

Antilog of $\mathbf{0.7506 = 5.631 \times 10^0}$

$$\mathbf{= 5.631}$$

Question 4: **Use the logarithm table to evaluate $\mathbf{0.5692 \div 0.00943}$**

Solution

find the logarithm value of the numbers

Number	***Standard Form***	***Logarithm Value***
0.5692 $\div$ 0.00943	5.692×10^0 9.43×10^{-3}	$\bar{1}.7553$ $-$ $\bar{3}.9745$
		$\mathbf{1.7808}$

Add the logarithm values of all the numbers given.

$$\bar{1}.7553 - \bar{3}.9745 = 1.\mathbf{7808}$$

Find the Anti log of the total value.

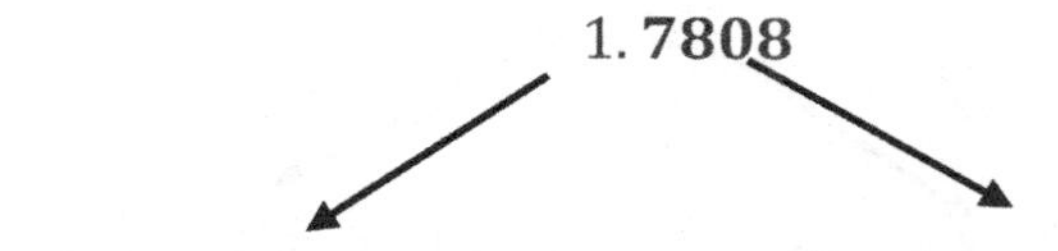

Integer (characteristics | **Decimal fraction (mantissa)**

Check the Antilogarithm table for:

$$The\ value\ of\ \mathbf{78}\ under\ \mathbf{0} = \mathbf{6026}$$

$$Mean\ difference\ of\ \mathbf{8} = \mathbf{11}$$

$$\mathbf{6026 + 11 = 6037}$$

Therefore,

Antilog of $\mathbf{1.7808 = 6.037 \times 10^1}$

$$\mathbf{= 60.37}$$

Question 5: **Use the logarithm table to evaluate** $\mathbf{0.7661 \div 0.3401}$

Solution

find the logarithm value of the numbers

Number	***Standard Form***	***Logarithm Value***
0.7661	7.661×10^{-1}	$\bar{1}.8843$
$\div$		$-$
0.3401	3.401×10^{-1}	$\bar{1}.5316$
		$\mathbf{0.3527}$

Add the logarithm values of all the numbers given.

$$\bar{1}.8843 - \bar{3}.5316 = 0.\mathbf{3527}$$

Find the Anti log of the total value.

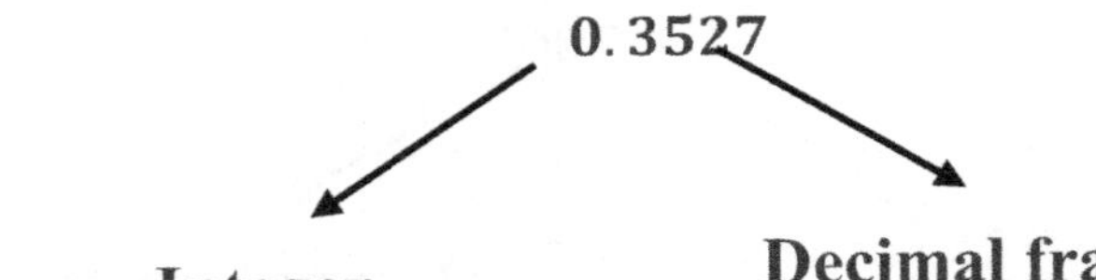

Check the Antilogarithm table for:

$$The\ value\ of\ \mathbf{35}\ under\ \mathbf{2}\ =\ \mathbf{2249}$$

$$Mean\ difference\ of\ \mathbf{7} = \mathbf{4}$$

$$\mathbf{2249 + 4 = 2253}$$

Therefore,

Antilog of $\mathbf{0.3527 = 2.253 \times 10^0}$

$$\mathbf{= 2.253}$$

Question 6: **Use the logarithm table to evaluate** $\mathbf{0.3425 \div 0.1937}$

Solution

find the logarithm value of the numbers

Number	***Standard Form***	***Logarithm Value***
0.3425	3.425×10^{-1}	$\bar{1}.5346$
÷		−
0.1937	1.937×10^{-3}	$\bar{1}.2872$
		$\mathbf{0.2574}$

Add the logarithm values of all the numbers given.

$$\bar{1}.5346 - \bar{1}.2872 = 0.\mathbf{2574}$$

Find the Anti log of the total value.

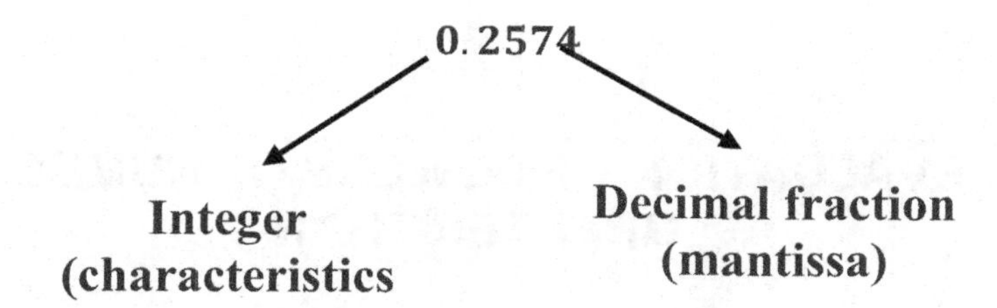

Check the Antilogarithm table for:

$$\textit{The value of } \mathbf{25} \textit{ under } \mathbf{7} = \mathbf{1807}$$

$$\textit{Mean difference of } \mathbf{4} = \mathbf{2}$$

$$\mathbf{1807 + 2 = 1809}$$

Therefore,

Antilog of $\mathbf{0.2574 = 1.809 \times 10^0}$

$\mathbf{= 1.809}$

Unit 12

EVALUATION OF POWERS OF NUMBERS GREATER THAN 1

How can you use logarithm table to evaluate numbers with powers?

Steps

1. Rewrite the number in standard form.
2. Express the coefficient as logarithm, that is find the logarithm value of the coefficient.
3. Multiply the logarithm values of the coefficients with the exponent.
4. Find the Antilog of the total value.

Question 1: **Use the logarithm table to evaluate 3.55^4**

Solution

find the logarithm value of the numbers

Number	*Standard Form*	*Logarithm Value*
3.55	3.55×10^0	0.5502
		×
3.55^4		4
		2.2008

The logarithm values = 2.2008

Find the Anti log of the total value.

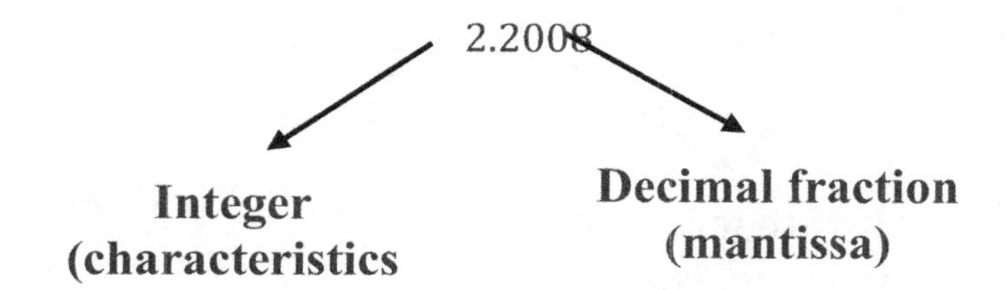

Check the Antilogarithm table for:

$$The\ value\ of\ \mathbf{20}\ under\ \mathbf{0}\ =\ \mathbf{1585}$$

$$Mean\ difference\ of\ \mathbf{8 = 3}$$

$$\mathbf{1585 + 3 = 1588}$$

Therefore,

Antilog of $\mathbf{2.2008 = 1.588 \times 10^2}$

$$\mathbf{= 158.8}$$

Question 2: **Use the logarithm table to evaluate $\mathbf{57.78^3}$**

Solution

find the logarithm value of the numbers

Number	Standard Form	Logarithm Value
57.78	5.778×10^1	1.7618
		$\times$
57.78^3		3
		5.2854

The logarithm values = 2.2854

Find the Anti log of the total value.

Integer (characteristics

Decimal fraction (mantissa)

Check the Antilogarithm table for:

$$The\ value\ of\ \mathbf{28}\ under\ \mathbf{5}\ =\ \mathbf{1928}$$

$$Mean\ difference\ of\ \mathbf{4} = \mathbf{2}$$

$$\mathbf{1928 + 2 = 1930}$$

Therefore,

Antilog of $\mathbf{5.2854 = 1.930 \times 10^5}$

$$\mathbf{= 193000}$$

Question 3: **Use the logarithm table to evaluate** $\mathbf{43.47^2} \times \mathbf{23.45^3}$

Solution

find the logarithm value of the numbers

Number	***Standard Form***	***Logarithm Value***	
43.47	4.347×10^1	1.6412 × 2	
43.47^2			
		2.2824	2.2824
23.45	2.345×10^1	1.3699 × 3	
23.45^3			

		4.1097	4.1097
			$6,3921$

The logarithm values = 6.3921

Find the Anti log of the total value.

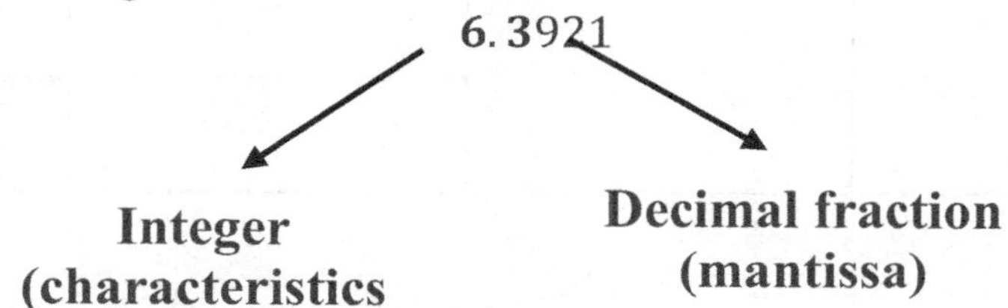

Check the Antilogarithm table for:

$$The\ value\ of\ \mathbf{39}\ under\ \mathbf{2}\ =\ \mathbf{2466}$$

$$Mean\ difference\ of\ \mathbf{1} = \mathbf{1}$$

$$\mathbf{2466 + 1 = 2467}$$

Therefore,

Antilog of $\mathbf{6.3921 = 2.467 \times 10^6}$

$$\mathbf{= 2467000}$$

Question 4: **Use the logarithm table to evaluate** $\left(\frac{143.7}{7.3}\right)^5$

Solution

find the logarithm value of the numbers

Number	***Standard Form***	***Logarithm Value***	
143.7 7.3	1.437×10^2 7.3×10^0	2.1574 − 0.8633	

$\left(\frac{143.7}{7.3}\right)^5$		**1.2941**	1.2941
			$\times$ 5
			6.4705

The logarithm values = 6.4705

Find the Anti log of the total value.

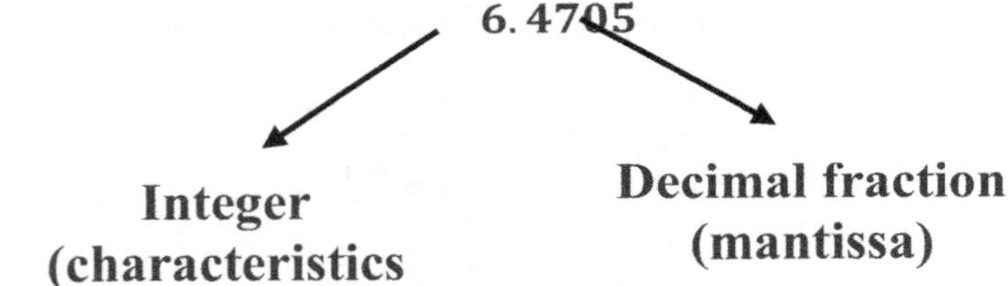

Check the Antilogarithm table for:

$$The\ value\ of\ \mathbf{47}\ under\ \mathbf{0}\ =\ \mathbf{2951}$$

$$Mean\ difference\ of\ \mathbf{5} = \mathbf{5}$$

$$\mathbf{2951 + 5 = 2956}$$

Therefore,

Antilog of $\mathbf{6.4705 = 2.956 \times 10^6}$

$$\mathbf{= 2956000}$$

Question 5: **Use the logarithm table to evaluate 78.93^3**

Solution

find the logarithm value of the numbers

Number	Standard Form	Logarithm Value
78.93	7.893×10^1	1.8973
		$\times$
78.93^3		3
		5.6919

The logarithm values = 5.6919
Find the Anti log of the total value.

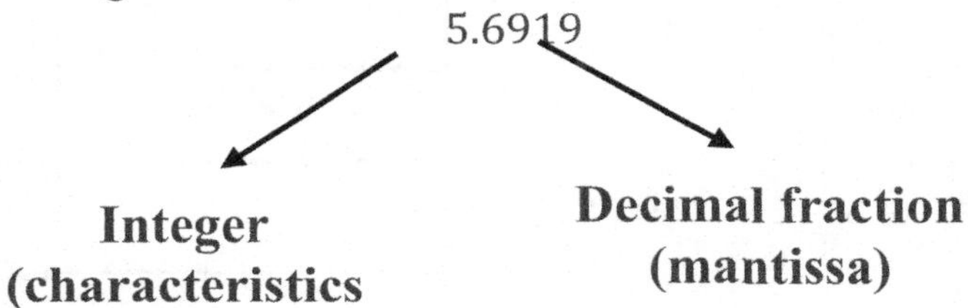

Check the Antilogarithm table for:

$$The\ value\ of\ \mathbf{69}\ under\ \mathbf{1}\ =\ \mathbf{4909}$$

$$Mean\ difference\ of\ \mathbf{9} = \mathbf{10}$$

$$\mathbf{4909 + 1 = 4910}$$

Therefore,

Antilog of $\mathbf{5.6919 = 4.910 \times 10^5}$

$$\mathbf{= 491000}$$

Question 6: **Use the logarithm table to evaluate $\mathbf{2.632^2 \times 53.67^3}$**

Solution
find the logarithm value of the numbers

Number	Standard Form	Logarithm Value	

2.632 2.632^3	2.632×10^1	0.4203 $\times$ 3	
		1.2609	1.2609
53.67 53.67^2	5.367×10^1	1.7298 $\times$ 2	
		3.4596	**3.4596**
			4.7205

The logarithm values = 4.7205

Find the Anti log of the total value.

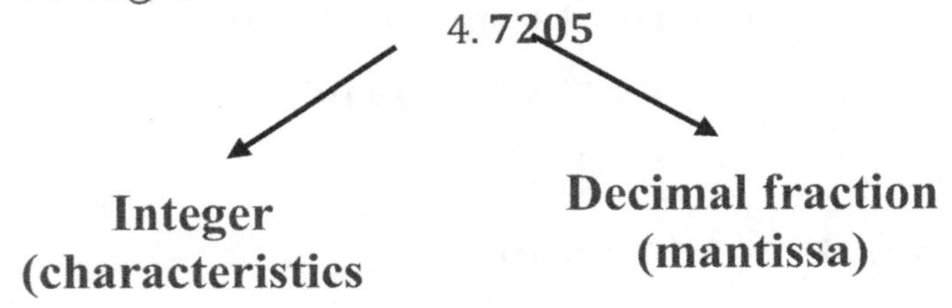

Check the Antilogarithm table for:

$$The\ value\ of\ \mathbf{72}\ under\ \mathbf{0}\ =\ \mathbf{5248}$$

$$Mean\ difference\ of\ \mathbf{5} = \mathbf{6}$$

$$\mathbf{5248 + 6 = 5254}$$

Therefore,

Antilog of $\mathbf{4.7205 = 5.254 \times 10^4}$

$$= \mathbf{52540}$$

Unit 13

EVALUATION OF ROOTS OF NUMBERS GREATER THAN 1

How can you use logarithm table to evaluate numbers with root?

Steps

1. Rewrite the number in standard form.
2. Express the coefficient as logarithm, that is find the logarithm value of the coefficient.
3. Divide the logarithm values of the coefficients with the exponent.
4. Find the Antilog of the total value.

Question 1: **Use the logarithm table to Evaluate $\sqrt[3]{20.45}$**

Solution

find the logarithm value of the numbers

Number	***Standard Form***	***Logarithm Value***
20.45	2.045×10^1	1.3107
		÷
$\sqrt[3]{20.45}$		3
		0.4369

The logarithm values = 0.4369

Find the ***Anti log*** *of the value*

.

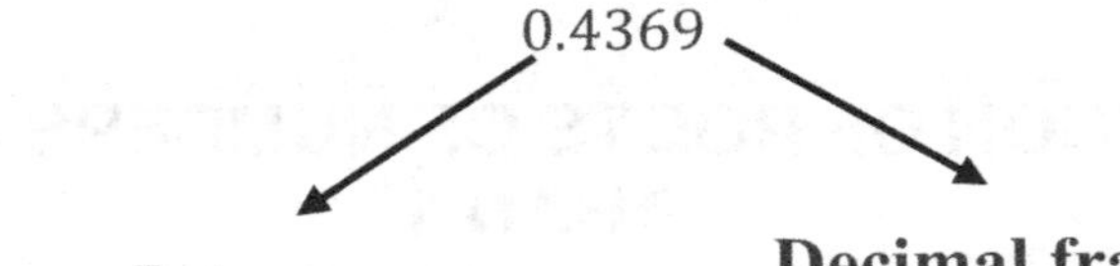

Check the Antilogarithm table for:

$$\textit{The value of } \mathbf{43} \textit{ under } \mathbf{6} = \mathbf{2729}$$

$$\textit{Mean difference of } \mathbf{8} = \mathbf{6}$$

$$\mathbf{2729 + 6 = 2735}$$

Therefore,

Antilog of $\mathbf{0.4369 = 2.735 \times 10^0}$

$$\mathbf{= 2.735 \times 1 = 2.735}$$

Question 2: **Use the logarithm table to Evaluate** $\sqrt[6]{\mathbf{83.53}}$

Solution

find the logarithm value of the numbers

Number	Standard Form	Logarithm Value
83.53	8.353×10^1	1.9220
$\sqrt[6]{83.53}$		$\div$ 6
		0.3203

The logarithm values = 0.3203

*Find the **Anti log** of the value.*

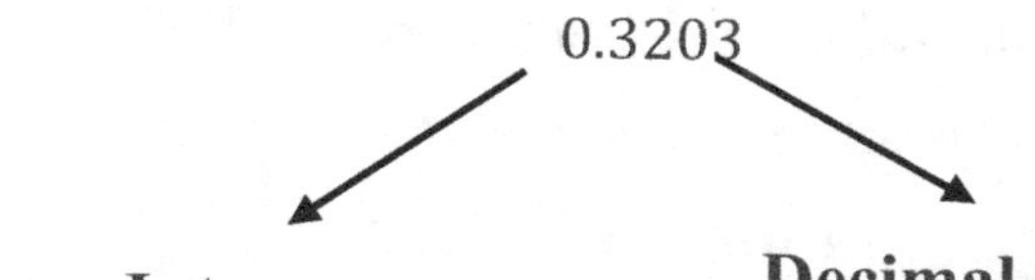

Integer (characteristics

Decimal fraction (mantissa)

Check the Antilogarithm table for:

$$\textit{The value of } \mathbf{32} \textit{ under } \mathbf{0} = \mathbf{2089}$$

$$\textit{Mean difference of } \mathbf{3} = \mathbf{3}$$

$$\mathbf{2089 + 3 = 2092}$$

Therefore,

Antilog of $\mathbf{0.3203 = 2.092 \times 10^0}$

$$\mathbf{= 2.092 \times 1 = 2.092}$$

Question 3: **Use the logarithm table to Evaluate** $\sqrt[3]{2750000}$

Solution

find the logarithm value of the numbers

Number	***Standard Form***	***Logarithm Value***
2750000	2.75×10^6	6.4393
		÷
$\sqrt[3]{2750000}$		3
		2.1464

The logarithm values = 2.1464

Find the ***Anti log*** *of the value.*

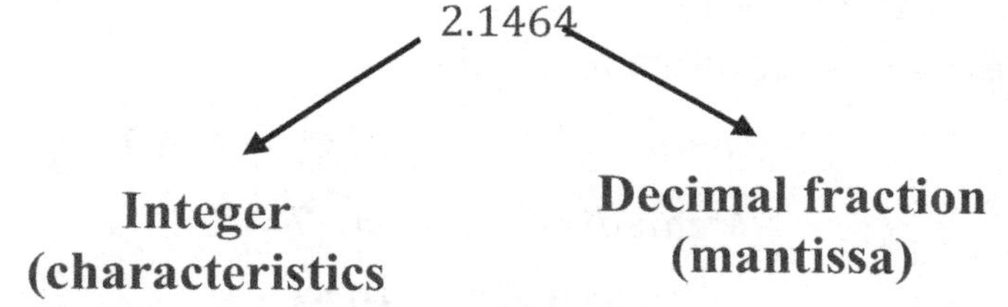

Check the Antilogarithm table for:

$$\textit{The value of } \mathbf{14} \textit{ under } \mathbf{6} = 1400$$

$$\textit{Mean difference of } \mathbf{4} = \mathbf{1}$$

$$\mathbf{1400 + 1 = 1401}$$

Therefore,

Antilog of $2.1464 = \mathbf{1.401 \times 10^2}$

$$= \mathbf{1.401 \times 100 = 140.1}$$

Question 4: **Use the logarithm table to Evaluate** $\sqrt[7]{93.7}$

Solution

find the logarithm value of the numbers

Number	**Standard Form**	**Logarithm Value**
93.7	9.37×10^1	1.9717
		÷
$\sqrt[7]{93.7}$		7
		0.2817

The logarithm values = 0.2817

Find the ***Anti log*** *of the value.*

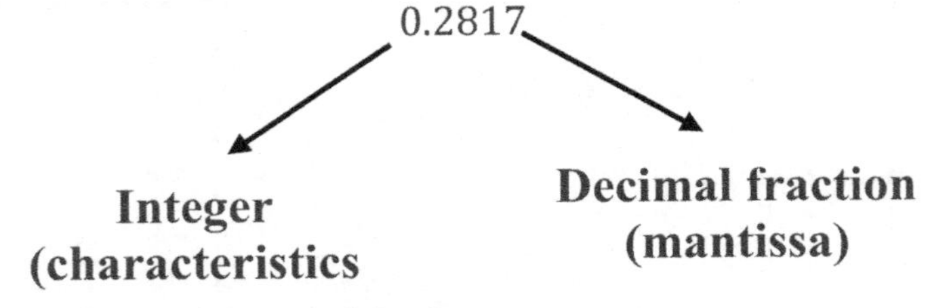

Check the Antilogarithm table for:

$$\textit{The value of } \mathbf{28} \textit{ under } \mathbf{1} = \mathbf{1910}$$

$$\textit{Mean difference of } \mathbf{7} = \mathbf{3}$$

$$\mathbf{1910 + 3 = 1913}$$

Therefore,

Antilog of $\mathbf{0.2817 = 1913 \times 10^0}$

$$\mathbf{= 1.910 \times 1 = 1.913}$$

Question 5: **Use the logarithm table to Evaluate** $\mathbf{\sqrt{87.5 \times 56.4}}$

Solution

find the logarithm value of the numbers

Number	***Standard Form***	***Logarithm Value***	
87.5	8.75×10^1	1..9420 +	
56.4	5.64×10^1	1.7513	
		3.6983	
$\sqrt{87.5 \times 56.4}$		3.6983 ÷ 2	
		1.8467	
			1.8467

The logarithm values = 1.8467

Find the ***Anti log*** *of the value.*

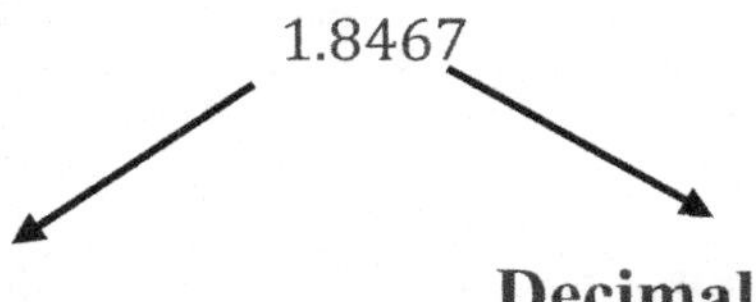

Integer (characteristics

Decimal fraction (mantissa)

Check the Antilogarithm table for:

$$The\ value\ of\ \mathbf{84}\ under\ \mathbf{6}\ =\ \mathbf{7015}$$

$$Mean\ difference\ of\ \mathbf{7} = \mathbf{11}$$

$$\mathbf{7015 + 11 = 7026}$$

Therefore,

Antilog of $\mathbf{1.8467 = 7.026 \times 10^1}$

$$\mathbf{= 7.026 \times 10 = 70.26}$$

Unit 14

EVALUATION OF NUMBERS LESS THAN 1 WITH POWERS

Steps for solving questions

1. Rewrite the number in standard form.
2. Express the coefficient as logarithm, that is find the logarithm value of the coefficient.
3. Multiply the logarithm values of the coefficients with the exponent.
4. Find the Antilog of the value.

Question 1: **Use the logarithm table to evaluate 0.7345^3**

Solution

find the logarithm value of the numbers

Number	*Standard Form*	*Logarithm Value*
0.7345	7.345×10^{-1}	$\bar{1}.8660$
		$\times$
0.7345^3		3
		$\bar{1}.5980$

The logarithm values = $\bar{1}.5980$

Find the ***Anti log*** *of the total value.*

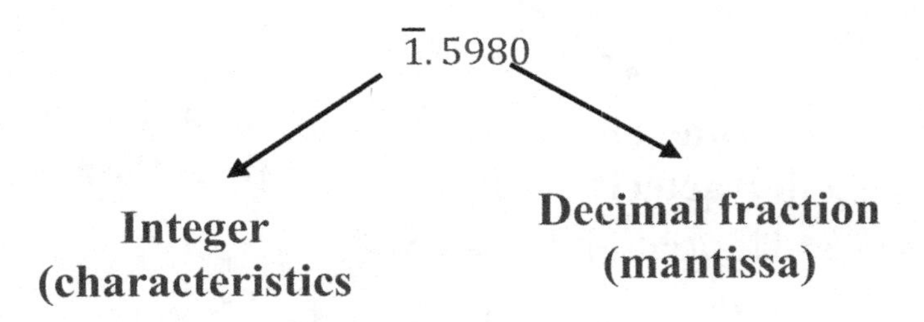

Check the Antilogarithm table for:

$$\textit{The value of } \mathbf{59} \textit{ under } \mathbf{8} = \mathbf{3963}$$

$$\textit{Mean difference of } \mathbf{0 = 0}$$

$$\mathbf{3963 + 0 = 3963}$$

Therefore,

Antilog of $\overline{1}.5980 = \mathbf{3.963 \times 10^{-1}}$

$$= \mathbf{0.3963}$$

Question 2: **Use the logarithm table to evaluate $\mathbf{0.07235^6}$**

Solution

find the logarithm value of the numbers

Number	***Standard Form***	***Logarithm Value***
0.07235	7.235×10^{-2}	$\overline{2}.8594$
		$\times$
0.07235^6		6
		$\overline{7}.1564$

The logarithm values = $\overline{7}.1564$

Find the ***Anti log*** *of the total value.*

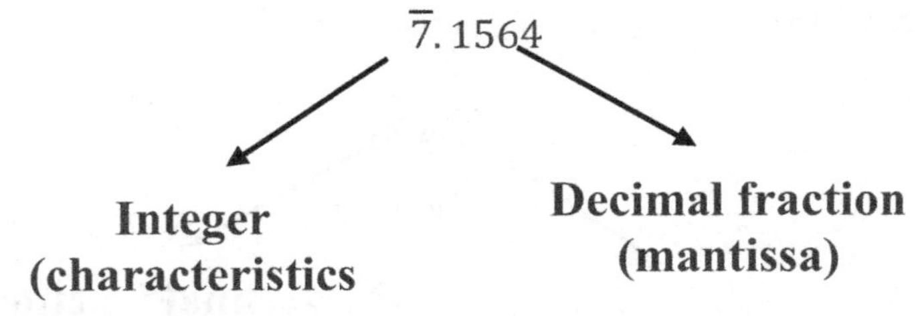

Check the Antilogarithm table for:

$$\textit{The value of } \mathbf{15} \textit{ under } \mathbf{6} = \mathbf{1432}$$

$$Mean\ difference\ of\ \mathbf{4 = 2}$$

$$\mathbf{1432 + 2 = 1434}$$

Therefore,

Antilog of $\overline{7}.1564 = \mathbf{1.434 \times 10^{-7}}$

$$= \mathbf{0.0000001434}$$

Question 3: **Use the logarithm table to evaluate** $\mathbf{0.6735^3}$

Solution

find the logarithm value of the numbers

Number	***Standard Form***	***Logarithm Value***
0.6735	6.735×10^{-1}	$\overline{1}.8283$
		$\times$
0.6735^3		3
		$\overline{1}.4849$

The logarithm values = $\overline{1}.4849$

*Find the **Anti log** of the total value.*

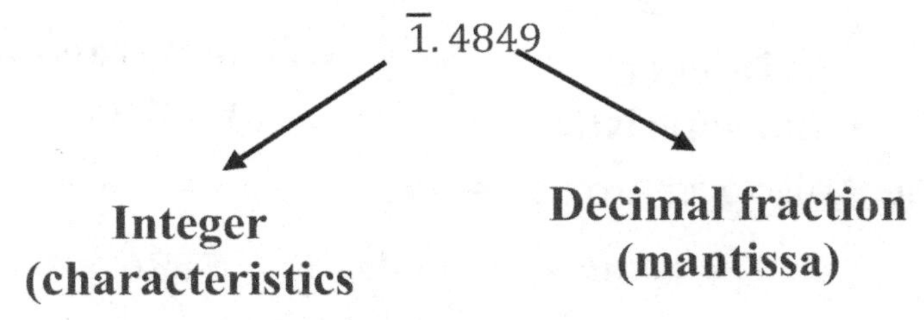

Check the Antilogarithm table for:

$$The\ value\ of\ \mathbf{48}\ under\ \mathbf{4 = 3048}$$

$$Mean\ difference\ of\ \mathbf{9 = 6}$$

$$\mathbf{3048 + 6 = 3054}$$

Therefore,

Antilog of $\bar{1}.4849 = \mathbf{3.048 \times 10^{-1}}$

$$= \mathbf{0.3054}$$

Question 4: **Use the logarithm table to evaluate** $\mathbf{0.4875^4}$

Solution

find the logarithm value of the numbers

Number	Standard Form	Logarithm Value
0.4875	4.875×10^{-1}	$\bar{1}.6879$
		$\times$
0.4875^4		4
		$\bar{2}.7516$

The logarithm values = $\bar{2}.7516$

Find the ***Anti log*** *of the total value.*

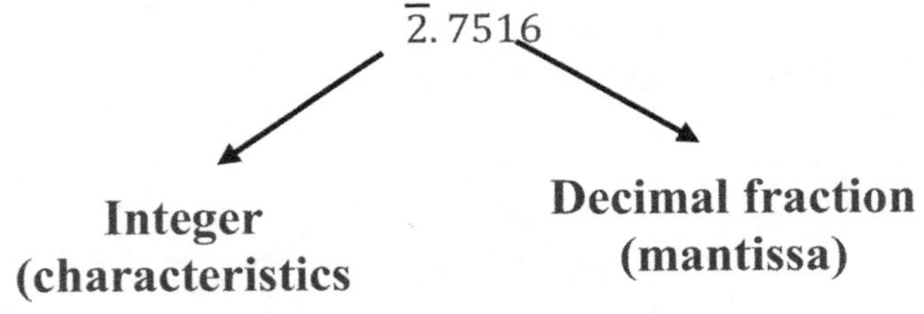

Check the Antilogarithm table for:

$$The\ value\ of\ \mathbf{75}\ under\ \mathbf{1}\ =\ \mathbf{5636}$$

$$Mean\ difference\ of\ \mathbf{6} = \mathbf{8}$$

$$\mathbf{3963 + 0 = 5644}$$

Therefore,

Antilog of $\bar{2}.7516 = \mathbf{5.644 \times 10^{-2}}$

$$= \mathbf{0.05644}$$

Question 5: **Use the logarithm table to evaluate $\mathbf{0.9356^7}$**

Solution

Find the logarithm value of the numbers

Number	***Standard Form***	***Logarithm Value***
0.9356	9.356×10^{-1}	$\bar{1}.9711$
		$\times$
0.9356^7		7
		$\bar{1}.7977$

The logarithm values = $\bar{1}.7977$

*Find the **Anti log** of the total value.*

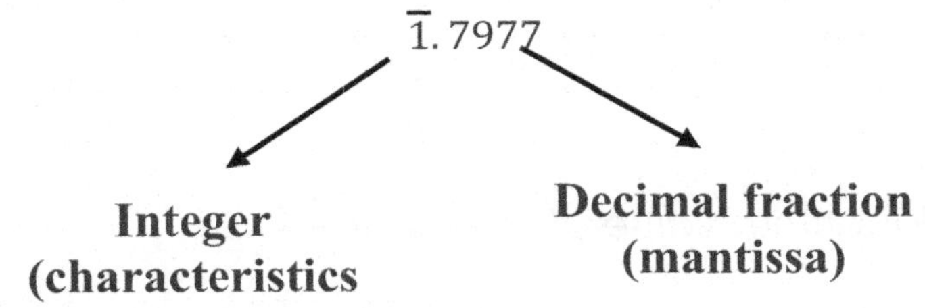

Check the Antilogarithm table for:

$$\textit{The value of } \mathbf{79} \textit{ under } \mathbf{7} = \mathbf{6266}$$

$$\textit{Mean difference of } \mathbf{7} = \mathbf{10}$$

$$\mathbf{6266 + 10 = 6276}$$

Therefore,

Antilog of $\bar{1}.5980 = \mathbf{3.963 \times 10^{-1}}$

$$= \mathbf{0.3963}$$

Unit 15

EVALUATION OF NUMBERS LESS THAN 1 WITH ROOTS

Steps

1. Rewrite the number in standard form.
2. Express the coefficient as logarithm, that is find the logarithm value of the coefficient.
3. Divide the logarithm values of the coefficients with the exponent.
4. Find the Antilog of the total value.

Question 1: **Use the logarithm table to Evaluate** $\sqrt[3]{\mathbf{0.0006956}}$

Solution

find the logarithm value of the numbers

Number	***Standard Form***	***Logarithm Value***
0.0006956	6.956×10^{-4}	$\bar{4}.8424$
		$\div$
$\sqrt[3]{0.0006956}$		3
		$\bar{2}.9475$

$$\frac{\bar{\mathbf{4}}.\mathbf{8424}}{\mathbf{3}} = \frac{\bar{4} + 0.8424}{3}$$

Factors of $\bar{\mathbf{4}}$ *that will make it divisible by* $\mathbf{3} = \bar{\mathbf{6}} + \mathbf{2}$

Substitute $\bar{\mathbf{6}} + \mathbf{2}$ *for* $\bar{\mathbf{4}}$

$$= \frac{\bar{4} + 0.8424}{3} = \frac{\bar{6} + 2 + 0.8424}{3}$$

$$= \frac{\bar{6} + 2.8424}{3}$$

$$= \frac{\bar{6}}{3} + \frac{2.8424}{3}$$

$$= \bar{2} + 0.9475 = \mathbf{\bar{2}.9475}$$

The logarithm values = $\mathbf{\bar{2}.9475}$

Find the ***Anti log*** *of the value.*

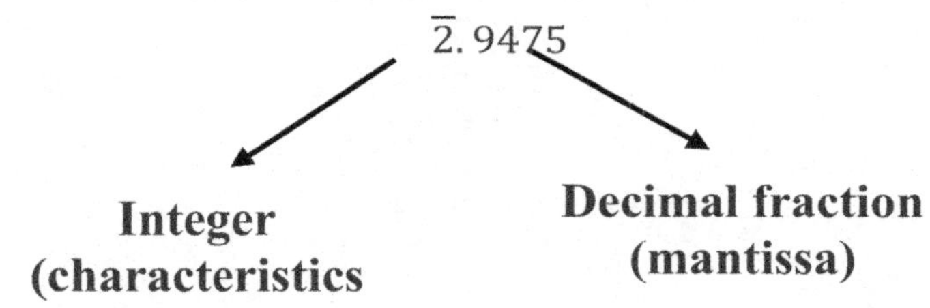

Check the Antilogarithm table for:

$$\textit{The value of } \mathbf{94} \textit{ under } \mathbf{7} = \mathbf{8851}$$

$$\textit{Mean difference of } \mathbf{5} = \mathbf{10}$$

$$\mathbf{8851 + 10 = 8861}$$

Therefore,

Antilog of $\bar{2}.9475 = \mathbf{8.861 \times 10^{-2}}$

$$= \mathbf{0.08861}$$

Question 2: **Use the logarithm table to Evaluate** $\sqrt[4]{\mathbf{0.087}}$

Solution

find the logarithm value of the numbers

Number	***Standard Form***	***Logarithm Value***

0.087 $\sqrt[4]{0.087}$	8.7×10^{-2}	$\bar{2}.9395$ $\div$ 4 $\bar{1}.7349$

$$\frac{\mathbf{\bar{2}.9395}}{\mathbf{4}} = \frac{\bar{2} + 0.9395}{4}$$

Factors of $\mathbf{\bar{2}}$ *that will make it divisible by* $4 = \mathbf{\bar{4} + 2}$

Substitute $\mathbf{\bar{4} + 2}$ *for* $\mathbf{\bar{2}}$

$$= \frac{\bar{2} + 0.9395}{4} = \frac{\bar{4} + 2 + 0.9395}{4}$$

$$= \frac{\bar{4} + 2.9395}{4}$$

$$= \frac{\bar{4}}{4} + \frac{2.9395}{4}$$

$$= \bar{1} + 0.7349 = \mathbf{\bar{1}.7349}$$

The logarithm values = $\mathbf{\bar{1}.7349}$

Find the ***Anti log*** *of the value.*

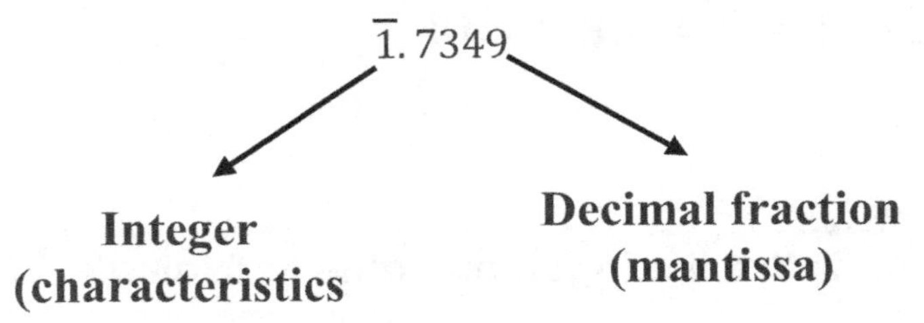

Check the Antilogarithm table for:

$$The\ value\ of\ \mathbf{73}\ under\ \mathbf{4}\ =\ \mathbf{5420}$$

$$Mean\ difference\ of\ \mathbf{9} = \mathbf{11}$$

$$\mathbf{5420 + 11 = 5431}$$

Therefore,

Antilog of $\bar{1}.7349 = \mathbf{5.431 \times 10^{-1}}$

$$= \mathbf{0.5431}$$

Question 3: **Use the logarithm table to Evaluate** $\sqrt[3]{\mathbf{0.6821 \times 0.05934}}$

Solution

find the logarithm value of the numbers

Number	***Standard Form***	***Logarithm Value***	
0.6821	6.821×10^{-1}	$\bar{1}.8339$	
		+	
0.05934	5.934×10^{-2}	$\bar{2}.7734$	
		$\bar{2}.6073$	
		$\bar{2}.6073$	
$\sqrt[3]{0.6821 \times 0.05934}$		÷	
		3	
		$\mathbf{\bar{1}.5358}$	
			$\mathbf{\bar{1}.5358}$

$$\frac{\mathbf{\bar{2}.6073}}{\mathbf{3}} = \frac{\bar{2} + 0.6073}{3}$$

Factors of $\mathbf{\bar{1}}$ *that will make it divisible by* $3 = \mathbf{\bar{3} + 1}$

Substitute $\mathbf{\bar{3} + 1}$ *for* $\mathbf{\bar{2}}$

$$= \frac{\bar{2} + 0.6073}{3} = \frac{\bar{3} + 1 + 0.6073}{3}$$

$$= \frac{\bar{3} + 1.6073}{3}$$

$$= \frac{\bar{3}}{3} + \frac{1.6073}{3}$$

$$= \bar{1} + 0.5358 = \mathbf{\bar{1}.5358}$$

The logarithm values = $\mathbf{\bar{1}.5358}$

*Find the **Anti log** of the value.*

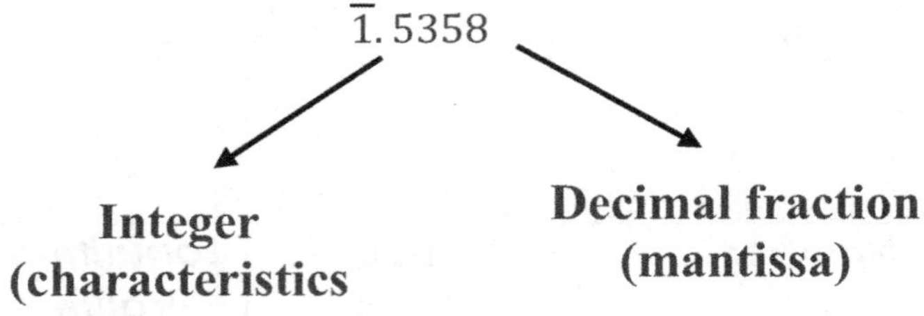

Check the Antilogarithm table for:

$$The\ value\ of\ \mathbf{53}\ under\ \mathbf{5}\ =\ \mathbf{3428}$$

$$Mean\ difference\ of\ \mathbf{8} = \mathbf{6}$$

$$\mathbf{3428 + 6 = 3434}$$

Therefore,

Antilog of $\bar{1}.5358 = \mathbf{3.434 \times 10^{-1}}$

$$= \mathbf{0.3434}$$

Question 4: **Use the logarithm table to Evaluate** $\sqrt[3]{\mathbf{(0.2875)^2}}$

Solution

find the logarithm value of the numbers

Number	***Standard Form***	***Logarithm Value***	
0.2875	2.875×10^{-1}	$\bar{1}.4587$	
		$\times$	
$(0.2875)^2$		2	
		$\bar{2}.9174$	

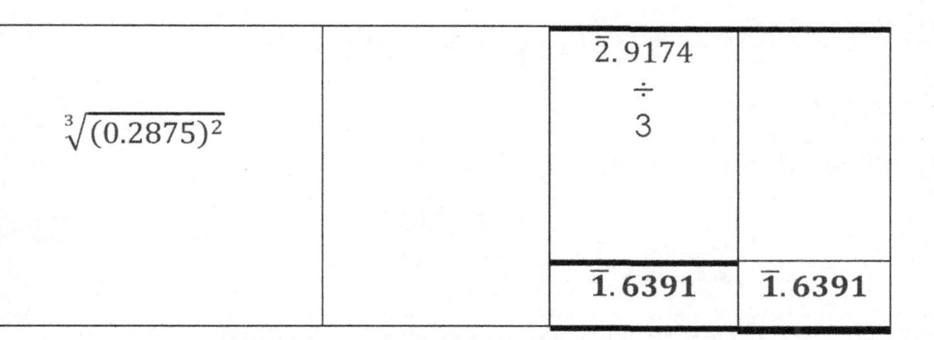

$\sqrt[3]{(0.2875)^2}$		$\bar{2}.9174$ $\div$ 3	
		$\mathbf{\bar{1}.6391}$	$\mathbf{\bar{1}.6391}$

$$\frac{\mathbf{\bar{2}.9174}}{\mathbf{3}} = \frac{\bar{2} + 0.9174}{3}$$

Factors of $\mathbf{\bar{2}}$ *that will make it divisible by* $3 = \mathbf{\bar{3} + 1}$

Substitute $\mathbf{\bar{3} + 1}$ *for* $\mathbf{\bar{2}}$

$$= \frac{\bar{2} + 0.9174}{3} = \frac{\bar{3} + 1 + 0.9395}{3}$$

$$= \frac{\bar{3} + 1.9174}{3}$$

$$= \frac{\bar{3}}{3} + \frac{1.9174}{3}$$

$$= \bar{1} + 0.6391 = \mathbf{\bar{1}.6391}$$

The logarithm values = $\mathbf{\bar{1}.6391}$

Find the ***Anti log*** *of the value.*

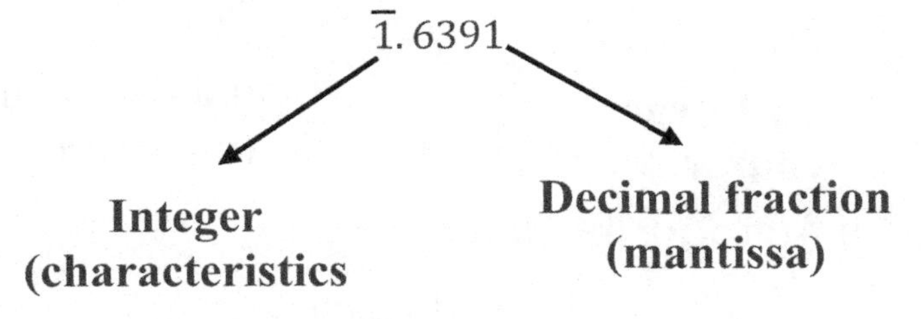

Check the Antilogarithm table for:

$$\textit{The value of } \mathbf{63} \textit{ under } \mathbf{9} = \mathbf{4355}$$

$$\textit{Mean difference of } \mathbf{1} = \mathbf{1}$$

$$\mathbf{4355 + 1 = 4356}$$

Therefore,

Antilog of $\bar{1}.6391 = \mathbf{4.356 \times 10^{-1}}$

$$= \mathbf{0.4356}$$

Question 5: **Use the logarithm table to Evaluate** $\sqrt[3]{\mathbf{0.00891}}$

Solution

find the logarithm value of the numbers

Number	***Standard Form***	***Logarithm Value***
0.00891	8.91×10^{-3}	$\bar{3}.9499$
		$\div$
$\sqrt[3]{0.00891}$		3
		$\bar{1}.3166$

The logarithm values = $\bar{\mathbf{1}}.\mathbf{3166}$

*Find the **Anti log** of the value.*

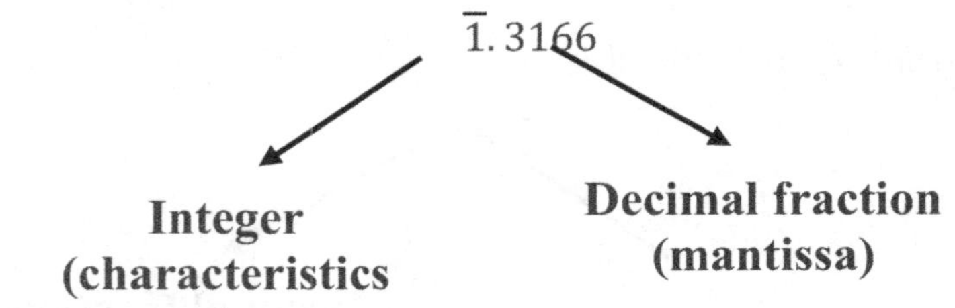

Check the Antilogarithm table for:

$$\textit{The value of } \mathbf{31} \textit{ under } \mathbf{6} \; = \; \mathbf{2070}$$

$$\textit{Mean difference of } \mathbf{6 = 3}$$

$$\mathbf{2070 + 3 = 2073}$$

Therefore,

Antilog of $\bar{1}.3166 = \mathbf{2.073 \times 10^{-1}}$

$= \mathbf{0.2073}$

GENERAL EXERCISE

1. Evaluate $\mathbf{12.31^2}$ using logarithm table.

Answer: 151.5

2. Evaluate $\mathbf{10.81 \times 23.82 \times 0.1041}$ using logarithm table.

Answer: 26.81

3. Evaluate $\mathbf{436.7 \div 20.47}$ using logarithm table.

Answer: 21.33

4. Evaluate $\mathbf{0.0004621 \div 0.08763}$ using logarithm table.

Answer: 0.05273

5. Evaluate $(\mathbf{6.423})^2 \times (\mathbf{4.314})^3$ using logarithm table.

Answer: 3312

6. Evaluate $\sqrt{\frac{2.65\times0.00714}{(20.21)^2}}$ using logarithm table.

Answer : 21.33

7. Evaluate $\sqrt{\mathbf{147.9}}$ using logarithm table.

Answer: 12.16

8. Evaluate $\sqrt{\mathbf{0.04570}}$ using logarithm table.

Answer: 0.2138

9. Simplify $\mathbf{\log_9 3 + \log_9 243 + 2\log_9 3}$

Answer: 2

10.Solve for x: $\log_2(x-3)+\log_2 x=2$

Answer:-1 or 4

11.Solve for x: $\log_{\sqrt{2}} 16 = x$

Answer: 8

12.Simplify: $2\log_3 8 - 3\log_3 2$

Answer: $2\log_3 2$

13.Simplify: $\log_4 4^x$

Answer : x

14.Solve for x: $\log_2(x^2 + 6x + 28) = 2$

Answer : 6 *or* -12

15.Solve for x: $\mathbf{\log_2(x^2 - 5x - 10) = 2}$

***Answer :* -2 *or* 7**

Logarithm Table

											Mean Differences								
	0	1	2	3	4	5	6	7	8	9	1	2	3	4	5	6	7	8	9
10	0000	0043	0086	0128	0017	0212	0253	0294	0334	0374	4	8	12	17	21	25	29	33	37
11	0414	0453	0492	0531	0569	0607	0645	0682	0719	0755	4	8	11	15	19	23	26	30	34
12	0792	0828	0864	0899	0934	0969	1004	1038	1072	1106	3	7	10	14	17	21	24	28	31
13	1139	1173	1206	1239	1271	1303	1335	1367	1399	1430	3	6	10	13	16	19	23	26	29
14	1461	1492	1523	1553	1584	1614	1644	1673	1703	1732	3	6	9	12	15	18	21	24	27
15	1761	1790	1818	1847	1875	1903	1931	1959	1987	2014	3	6	8	11	14	17	20	22	25
16	2041	2068	2095	2122	2148	2175	2201	2227	2253	2279	3	5	8	11	13	16	18	21	24
17	2304	2330	2355	2380	2405	2430	2455	2480	2504	2529	2	5	7	10	12	15	17	20	22
18	2553	2577	2601	2625	2648	2672	2695	2718	2742	2765	2	5	7	9	12	14	16	19	21
19	2788	2810	2833	2856	2878	2900	2923	2945	2967	2989	2	4	7	9	11	13	16	18	20
20	3010	3032	3054	3075	3096	3118	3139	3160	3181	3201	2	4	6	8	11	13	15	17	19
21	3222	3243	3263	3284	3304	3324	3345	3365	3385	3404	2	4	6	8	10	12	14	16	18
22	3424	3444	3464	3483	3502	3522	3541	2560	3579	3598	2	4	6	8	10	12	14	15	17
23	3617	3636	3655	3674	3692	3711	3729	3747	3766	3784	2	4	6	7	9	11	13	15	17
24	3802	3820	3838	3856	3874	3892	3909	3927	3945	3962	2	4	5	7	9	11	12	14	16
25	3979	3997	4014	4031	4048	4065	4082	4099	4116	4133	2	3	5	7	9	10	12	14	15
26	4150	4166	4183	4200	4216	4232	4249	4265	4281	4298	2	3	5	7	8	10	11	13	15
27	4314	4330	4346	4362	4378	4393	4409	4425	4440	4456	2	3	5	6	8	9	11	13	14
28	4472	4487	4502	4518	4533	4548	4564	4579	4594	4609	2	3	5	6	8	9	11	12	14
29	4624	4639	4654	4669	4683	4698	4713	4728	4742	4757	1	3	4	6	7	9	10	12	13
30	4771	4786	4800	4814	4829	4843	4857	4871	4886	4900	1	3	4	6	7	9	10	11	13
31	4914	4928	4942	4955	4969	4983	4997	5011	5024	5038	1	3	4	6	7	8	10	11	12
32	5051	5065	5079	5092	5105	5119	5132	5145	5159	5172	1	3	4	5	7	8	9	11	12
33	5185	5198	5211	5224	5237	5250	5263	5276	5289	5302	1	3	4	5	6	8	9	10	12
34	5315	5328	5340	5353	5366	5378	5391	5403	5416	5428	1	3	4	5	6	8	9	10	11
35	5441	5453	5465	5478	5490	5502	5514	5527	5539	5551	1	2	4	5	6	7	9	10	11
36	5563	5575	5587	5599	5611	5623	5635	5647	5658	5670	1	2	4	5	6	7	8	10	11
37	5682	5694	5705	5717	5729	5740	5752	5763	5775	5786	1	2	3	5	6	7	8	9	10
38	5798	5809	5821	5832	5843	5855	5866	5877	5888	5899	1	2	3	5	6	7	8	9	10
39	5911	5922	5933	5944	5955	5966	5977	5988	5999	6010	1	2	3	4	6	7	8	9	10
40	6021	6031	6042	6053	6064	6075	6085	6096	6107	6117	1	2	3	4	5	6	8	9	10
41	6128	6138	6149	6160	6170	6180	6191	6201	6212	6222	1	2	3	4	5	6	7	8	9
42	6232	6243	6253	6263	6274	6284	6294	6304	6314	6325	1	2	3	4	5	6	7	8	9
43	6335	6345	6355	6365	6375	6385	6395	6405	6415	6425	1	2	3	4	5	6	7	8	9
44	6435	6444	6454	6464	6474	6484	6493	6503	6513	6522	1	2	3	4	5	6	7	8	9
45	6532	6542	6551	6561	6571	6580	6590	6599	6609	6618	1	2	3	4	5	6	7	8	9
46	6628	6637	6646	6656	6665	6675	6684	6693	6702	6712	1	2	3	4	5	6	7	7	8
47	6721	6730	6739	6749	6758	6767	6776	6785	6794	6803	1	2	3	4	5	5	6	7	8
48	6812	6821	6830	6839	6848	6857	6866	6875	6884	6893	1	2	3	4	4	5	6	7	8
49	6902	6911	6920	6928	6937	6946	6955	6964	6972	6981	1	2	3	4	4	5	6	7	8
50	6990	6998	7007	7016	7024	7033	7042	7050	7059	7067	1	2	3	3	4	5	6	7	8

Logarithm Table

											Mean Differences								
51	7076	7084	7093	7101	7110	7118	7126	7135	7143	7152	1	2	3	3	4	5	6	7	8
52	7160	7168	7177	7185	7193	7202	7210	7218	7226	7235	1	2	2	3	4	5	6	7	7
53	7243	7251	7259	7267	7275	7284	7292	7300	7308	7316	1	2	2	3	4	5	6	6	7
54	7324	7332	7340	7348	7356	7364	7372	7380	7388	7396	1	2	2	3	4	5	6	6	7
55	7404	7412	7419	7427	7435	7443	7451	7459	7466	7474	1	2	2	3	4	5	5	6	7
56	7482	7490	7497	7505	7513	7520	7528	7536	7543	7551	1	2	2	3	4	5	5	6	7
57	7559	7566	7574	7582	7589	7597	7604	7612	7619	7627	1	2	2	3	4	5	5	6	7
58	7634	7642	7649	7657	7664	7672	7679	7686	7694	7701	1	1	2	3	4	4	5	6	7
59	7709	7716	7723	7731	7738	7745	7752	7760	7767	7774	1	1	2	3	4	4	5	6	7
60	7782	7789	7796	7803	7810	7818	7825	7832	7839	7846	1	1	2	3	4	4	5	6	6
61	7853	7860	7868	7875	7882	7889	7896	7903	7910	7917	1	1	2	3	4	4	5	6	6
62	7924	7931	7938	7945	7952	7959	7966	7973	7980	7987	1	1	2	3	3	4	5	6	6
63	7993	8000	8007	8014	8021	8028	8035	8041	8048	8055	1	1	2	3	3	4	5	5	6
64	8062	8069	8075	8082	8089	8096	8102	8109	8116	8122	1	1	2	3	3	4	5	5	6
65	8129	8136	8142	8149	8156	8162	8169	8176	8182	8189	1	1	2	3	3	4	5	5	6
66	8195	8202	8209	8215	8222	8228	8235	8241	8248	8254	1	1	2	3	3	4	5	5	6
67	8261	8267	8274	8280	8287	8293	8299	8306	8312	8319	1	1	2	3	3	4	5	5	6
68	8325	8331	8338	8344	8351	8357	8363	8370	8376	8382	1	1	2	3	3	4	4	5	6
69	8388	8395	8401	8407	8414	8420	8426	8432	8439	8445	1	1	2	3	3	4	4	5	6
70	8451	8457	8463	8470	8476	8482	8488	8494	8500	8506	1	1	2	2	3	4	4	5	6
71	8513	8519	8525	8531	8537	8543	8549	8555	8561	8567	1	1	2	2	3	4	4	5	5
72	8573	8579	8585	8591	8597	8603	8609	8615	8621	8627	1	1	2	2	3	4	4	5	5
73	8633	8639	8645	8651	8657	8663	8669	8675	8681	8686	1	1	2	2	3	4	4	5	5
74	8692	8698	8704	8710	8716	8722	8727	8733	8739	8745	1	1	2	2	3	3	4	5	5
75	8751	8756	8762	8768	8774	8779	8785	8791	8797	8802	1	1	2	2	3	3	4	5	5
76	8808	8814	882	8825	8831	8837	8842	8848	8854	8859	1	1	2	2	3	3	4	5	5
77	8865	8871	8876	8882	8887	8893	8899	8904	8910	8915	1	1	2	2	3	3	4	4	5
78	8921	8927	8932	8938	8943	8949	8954	8960	8965	8971	1	1	2	2	3	3	4	4	5
79	8976	8982	8987	8993	8998	9004	9009	9015	9020	9025	1	1	2	2	3	3	4	4	5
80	9031	9036	9042	9047	9053	9058	9063	9069	9074	9079	1	1	2	2	3	3	4	4	5
81	9085	9090	9096	9101	9106	9112	9117	9122	9128	9133	1	1	2	2	3	3	4	4	5
82	9138	9143	9149	9154	9159	9165	9170	9175	9180	9186	1	1	2	2	3	3	4	4	5
83	9191	9196	9201	9206	9212	9217	9222	9227	9232	9238	1	1	2	2	3	3	4	4	5
84	9243	9248	9253	9258	9263	9269	9274	9279	9284	9289	1	1	2	2	3	3	4	4	5
85	9294	9299	9304	9309	9315	9320	9325	9330	9335	9340	1	1	2	2	3	3	4	4	5
86	9345	9350	9355	9360	9365	9370	9375	9380	9385	9390	1	1	2	2	3	3	4	4	5
87	9395	9400	9405	9410	9415	9420	9425	9430	9435	9440	0	1	1	2	2	3	3	4	4
88	9445	9450	9455	9460	9465	9469	9474	9479	9484	9489	0	1	1	2	2	3	3	4	4
89	9494	9499	9504	9509	9513	9518	9523	9528	9533	9538	0	1	1	2	2	3	3	4	4
90	9542	9547	9552	9557	9562	9566	9571	9576	9581	9586	0	1	1	2	2	3	3	4	4
91	9590	9595	9600	9605	9609	9614	9619	9624	9628	9633	0	1	1	2	2	3	3	4	4
92	9638	9643	9647	9652	9657	9661	9666	9671	9675	9680	0	1	1	2	2	3	3	4	4
93	9685	9689	9694	9699	9703	9708	9713	9717	9722	9727	0	1	1	2	2	3	3	4	4
94	9731	9736	9741	9745	9750	9754	9759	9763	9768	9773	0	1	1	2	2	3	3	4	4
95	9777	9782	9786	9791	9795	9800	9805	9809	9814	9818	0	1	1	2	2	3	3	4	4
96	9823	9827	9832	9836	9841	9845	9850	9854	9859	9863	0	1	1	2	2	3	3	4	4
97	9868	9872	9877	9881	9886	9890	9894	9899	9903	9908	0	1	1	2	2	3	3	4	4
98	9912	9917	9921	9926	9930	9934	9939	9943	9948	9952	0	1	1	2	2	3	3	4	4
99	9956	9961	9965	9969	9974	9978	9983	9987	9991	9996	0	1	1	2	2	3	3	3	4

Antilogarithm Table

	Mathscode										Mean Differences								
.51	3236	3243	3251	3258	3266	3273	3281	3289	3296	3304	1	2	2	3	4	5	5	6	7
.52	3311	3319	3327	3334	3342	3350	3357	3365	3373	3381	1	2	2	3	4	5	5	6	7
.53	3388	3396	3404	3412	3420	3428	3436	3443	3451	3459	1	2	2	3	4	5	6	6	7
.54	3467	3475	3483	3491	3499	3508	3516	3524	3532	3540	1	2	2	3	4	5	6	6	7
.55	3548	3556	3565	3573	3581	3589	3597	3606	3614	3622	1	2	2	3	4	5	6	7	7
.56	3631	3639	3648	3656	3664	3673	3681	3690	3698	3707	1	2	3	3	4	5	6	7	8
.57	3715	3724	3733	3741	3750	3758	3767	3776	3784	3793	1	2	3	3	4	5	6	7	8
.58	3802	3811	3819	3828	3837	3846	3855	3864	3873	3882	1	2	3	4	4	5	6	7	8
.59	3890	3899	3908	3917	3926	3936	3945	3954	3963	3972	1	2	3	4	5	5	6	7	8
.60	3981	3990	3999	4009	4018	4027	4036	4046	4055	4064	1	2	3	4	5	6	6	7	8
.61	4074	4083	4093	4102	4111	4121	4130	4140	4150	4159	1	2	3	4	5	6	7	8	9
.62	4169	4178	4188	4198	4207	4217	4227	4236	4246	4256	1	2	3	4	5	6	7	8	9
.63	4266	4276	4285	4295	4305	4315	4325	4335	4345	4355	1	2	3	4	5	6	7	8	9
.64	4365	4374	4385	4395	4406	4416	4426	4436	4446	4457	1	2	3	4	5	6	7	8	9
.65	4467	4477	4487	4498	4508	4519	4529	4539	4550	4560	1	2	3	4	5	6	7	8	9
.66	4571	4581	4592	4603	4613	4624	4634	4645	4656	4667	1	2	3	4	5	6	7	9	10
.67	4677	4688	4699	4710	4721	4732	4742	4753	4764	4775	1	2	3	4	5	7	8	9	10
.68	4786	4797	4808	4819	4831	4842	4853	4864	4875	4887	1	2	3	4	6	7	8	9	10
.69	4898	4909	4920	4932	4943	4955	4966	4977	4989	5000	1	2	3	5	6	7	8	9	10
.70	5012	5023	5035	5047	5058	4070	5082	5093	5105	5117	1	2	4	5	6	7	8	9	11
.71	5129	5140	5152	5164	5176	5188	5200	5212	5224	5236	1	2	4	5	6	7	8	10	11
.72	5248	5260	5272	5284	5297	5309	5321	5333	5346	5358	1	2	4	5	6	7	9	10	11
.73	5370	5383	5395	5408	5420	5433	5445	5458	5470	5483	1	3	4	5	6	8	9	10	11
.74	5495	5508	5521	5534	5546	5559	5572	5585	5598	5610	1	3	4	5	6	8	9	10	12
.75	5623	5636	5649	5662	5675	5689	5702	5715	5728	5741	1	3	4	5	7	8	9	10	12
.76	5754	5768	5781	5794	5808	5821	5834	5848	5861	5875	1	3	4	5	7	8	9	11	12
.77	5888	5902	5916	5929	5943	5957	5970	5984	5998	6012	1	3	4	5	7	8	10	11	12
.78	6026	6039	6053	6067	6081	6095	6109	6124	6138	6152	1	3	4	6	7	8	10	11	13
.79	6166	6180	6194	6209	6223	6237	6252	6266	6281	6295	1	3	4	6	7	9	10	11	13
.80	6310	6324	6339	6353	6368	6383	6397	6415	6427	6442	1	3	4	6	7	9	10	12	13
.81	6457	6471	6486	6501	6516	6531	6546	6561	6577	6592	2	3	5	6	8	9	11	12	14
.82	6607	6622	6637	6653	6668	6683	6699	6714	6730	6745	2	3	5	6	8	9	11	12	14
.83	6761	6776	6792	6808	6823	6839	6855	6871	6887	6902	2	3	5	6	8	9	11	13	14
.84	6918	6934	6950	6966	6982	6998	7015	7031	7047	7063	2	3	5	6	8	10	11	13	15
.85	7079	7096	7112	7129	7145	7161	7178	7196	7211	7228	2	3	5	7	8	10	12	13	15
.86	7244	7261	7278	7295	7311	7328	7345	7362	7379	7396	2	3	5	7	8	10	12	13	15
.87	7413	7430	7447	7464	7482	7499	7516	7534	7551	7568	2	3	5	7	9	10	12	14	16
.88	7586	7603	7621	7638	7656	7674	7691	7709	7727	7745	2	4	5	7	9	11	12	14	16
.89	7762	7780	7798	7816	7834	7852	7870	7889	7907	7925	2	4	5	7	9	11	13	14	16
.90	7943	7962	7980	7998	8017	8035	8054	8072	8091	8110	2	4	6	7	9	11	13	15	17
.91	8128	8147	8166	8185	8204	8222	8241	8260	8279	8299	2	4	6	8	9	11	13	15	17
.92	8318	8337	8356	8275	8395	8414	8433	8453	8472	8492	2	4	6	8	10	12	14	15	17
.93	8511	8531	8551	8570	8590	8610	8630	8650	8670	8690	2	4	6	8	10	12	14	16	18
.94	8710	8730	8750	8770	8790	8810	8831	8851	8872	8892	2	4	6	8	10	12	14	16	18
.95	8913	8933	8954	8974	8995	9016	9036	9057	9078	9099	2	4	6	8	10	12	15	17	19
.96	9120	9141	9162	9183	9204	9226	9247	9268	9290	9311	2	4	6	8	11	13	15	17	19
.97	9333	9354	9376	9397	9419	####	9462	9484	9506	9528	2	4	7	9	11	13	15	17	20
.98	9550	9572	9594	9616	9638	9661	9683	9705	9727	9750	2	4	7	9	11	13	16	18	20
.99	9772	9795	9817	9840	9863	9886	9908	9931	9954	9977	2	5	7	9	11	14	16	18	20

Antilogarithm Table

	Mathscode										Mean Differences								
	0	1	2	3	4	5	6	7	8	9	1	2	3	4	5	6	7	8	9
.00	1002	1005	1007	1009	1012	1014	1016	1019	1021	0000	0	0	1	1	1	1	2	2	2
.01	1023	1026	1028	1030	1033	1035	1038	1040	1042	1045	0	0	1	1	1	1	2	2	2
.02	1047	1050	1052	1054	1057	1059	1062	1064	1067	1069	0	0	1	1	1	1	2	2	2
.03	1072	1074	1076	1079	1081	1084	1086	1089	1091	1094	0	0	1	1	1	1	2	2	2
.04	1096	1099	1102	1104	1107	1109	1112	1114	1117	1119	0	1	1	1	1	2	2	2	2
.05	1122	1125	1127	1130	1132	1135	1138	1140	1143	1146	0	1	1	1	1	2	2	2	2
.06	1148	1151	1153	1156	1159	1161	1164	1167	1169	1172	0	1	1	1	1	1	2	2	2
.07	1175	1178	1180	1183	1186	1189	1191	1194	1197	1199	0	1	1	1	1	2	2	2	2
.08	1202	1205	1208	1211	1213	1216	1219	1222	1225	1227	0	1	1	1	1	2	2	2	3
.09	1230	1233	1236	1239	1242	1245	1247	1250	1253	1256	0	1	1	1	1	2	2	2	3
.10	1259	1262	1265	1268	1271	1274	1276	1279	1282	1285	0	1	1	1	1	2	2	2	3
.11	1288	1291	1294	1297	1300	1303	1306	1309	1312	1315	0	1	1	1	2	2	2	2	3
.12	1318	1321	1324	1327	1330	1334	1337	1340	1343	1346	0	1	1	1	2	2	2	2	3
.13	1349	1352	1355	1358	1361	1365	1368	1371	1374	1377	0	1	1	1	2	2	2	3	3
.14	1380	1384	1387	1390	1393	1396	1400	1403	1406	1409	0	1	1	1	2	2	2	3	3
.15	1413	1416	1419	1422	1426	1429	1432	1435	1439	1442	0	1	1	1	2	2	2	3	3
.16	1445	1449	1452	1455	1459	1462	1466	1469	1472	1476	0	1	1	1	2	2	2	3	3
.17	1479	1483	1486	1489	1493	1496	1500	1503	1507	1510	0	1	1	1	2	2	2	3	3
.18	1514	1517	1521	1524	1528	1531	1535	1538	1542	1545	0	1	1	1	2	2	2	3	3
.19	1549	1552	1556	1560	1563	1567	1570	1574	1578	1581	0	1	1	1	2	2	3	3	3
.20	1585	1589	1592	1596	1600	1603	1607	1611	1614	1618	0	1	1	1	2	2	3	3	3
.21	1622	1626	1629	1633	1637	1641	1644	1648	1652	1656	0	1	1	2	2	2	3	3	3
.22	1660	1663	1667	1671	1675	1679	1683	1687	1690	1694	0	1	1	2	2	2	3	3	3
.23	1698	1702	1706	1710	1714	1718	722	1726	1730	1734	0	1	1	2	2	2	3	3	4
.24	1738	1742	1746	1750	1754	1758	1762	1766	1770	1774	0	1	1	2	2	2	3	3	4
.25	1778	1782	1786	1791	1795	1799	1803	1807	1811	1816	0	1	1	2	2	2	3	3	4
.26	1820	1821	1828	1832	1837	1841	1845	1849	1854	1858	0	1	1	2	2	3	3	3	4
.27	1862	1866	1871	1875	1879	1884	1888	1892	1897	1901	0	1	1	2	2	3	3	3	4
.28	1905	1910	1914	1919	1923	1928	1932	1936	1941	1945	0	1	1	2	2	3	3	4	4
.29	1950	1954	1959	1963	1968	1972	1977	1982	1986	1991	0	1	1	2	2	3	3	4	4
.30	1995	2000	2004	2009	2014	2018	2023	2028	2032	2037	0	1	1	2	2	3	3	4	4
.31	2042	2046	2051	2056	2061	2065	2070	2075	2080	2084	0	1	1	2	2	3	3	4	4
.32	2089	2094	2099	2104	2109	2113	2118	2123	2128	2133	0	1	1	2	2	3	3	4	4
.33	2138	2143	2148	2153	2158	2163	2168	2173	2178	2183	0	1	1	2	2	3	3	4	4
.34	2188	2193	2198	2203	2208	2213	2218	2223	2228	2234	1	1	2	2	3	3	4	4	5
.35	2239	2244	2249	2254	2259	2265	2270	2275	2280	2286	1	1	2	2	3	3	4	4	5
.36	2291	2296	2301	2307	2312	2317	2323	2328	2333	2339	1	1	2	2	3	3	4	4	5
.37	2344	2350	2355	2360	2366	2371	2377	2382	2388	2393	1	1	2	2	3	3	4	4	5
.38	2399	2404	2410	2415	2421	2427	2432	2438	2443	2449	1	1	2	2	3	3	4	4	5
.39	2455	2460	2466	2472	2477	2483	2489	2495	2500	2506	1	1	2	2	3	3	4	5	5
.40	2512	2518	2523	2529	2535	2541	2547	2553	2559	2564	1	1	2	2	3	4	4	5	5
.41	2570	2576	2582	2588	2594	2600	2606	2612	2618	2624	1	1	2	2	3	4	4	5	5
.42	2630	2636	2642	2649	2655	2661	2667	2673	2679	2685	1	1	2	2	3	4	4	5	6
.43	2692	2698	2704	2710	2716	2723	2729	2735	2742	2748	1	1	2	3	3	4	4	5	6
.44	2754	2761	2767	2773	2780	2786	2793	2799	2805	2812	1	1	2	3	3	4	4	5	6
.45	2818	2825	2831	2838	2844	2851	2858	2864	2871	2877	1	1	2	3	3	4	5	5	6
.46	2884	2891	2897	2904	2911	2917	2924	2931	2938	2944	1	1	2	3	3	4	5	5	6
.47	2951	2958	2965	2972	2970	2985	2992	2999	3006	3013	1	1	2	3	3	4	5	5	6
.48	3020	3027	3034	3041	3048	3055	3062	3069	3076	3083	1	1	2	3	4	4	5	6	6
.49	3090	3097	3105	3112	3119	3126	3133	3141	3148	3155	1	1	2	3	4	4	5	6	6
.50	3162	3170	3177	3184	3192	3199	3206	3214	3221	3228	1	1	2	2	4	4	5	6	7

Improve your Math Skills with other Books

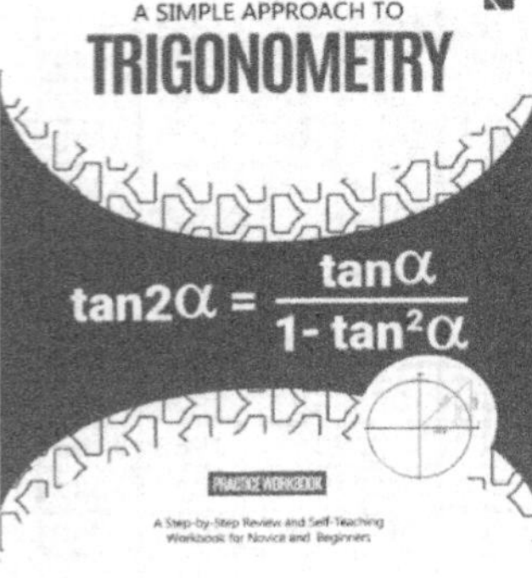

Made in the USA
Las Vegas, NV
07 January 2024